Butterflies of Dorset

Jeremy Thomas
and Nigel Webb

Maps prepared by
The Dorset Environmental Records Centre

1984

Dorset Natural History & Archaeological Society

Published by The Dorset Natural History & Archaeological Society,
Dorset County Museum, Dorchester, Dorset DT1 1XA. Editor: Jo Draper.
Printed by The Friary Press, Bridport Road, Dorchester.

British Library Cataloguing in Publication Data

Thomas, Jeremy
Butterflies of Dorset
1. Butterflies – England – Dorset – Identification
2. Insects – England – Dorset – Identification
I. Title. II. Webb, Nigel
595.78'9'094233 QL555.G7

ISBN 0-900341-21-1
ISBN 0-900341-20-1 Pbk

This publication was assisted by a loan from World Wildlife Fund

Contents

James Charles Dale, 1791-1872.

Preface

In 1886 C. W. Dale published the *Lepidoptera of Dorsetshire*, which he revised in 1891. For the next 60 years the County lists were kept under constant revision by Dorset entomologists, and two major works were prepared. Unfortunately, neither was fully published, and the accounts of the butterflies remain in manuscript. During the last 30 years, the status of most species has changed profoundly and the need for a new assessment was evident. To meet this there has been a decade of thorough survey and monitoring of the butterflies, with which we have been involved.

In this book, we draw upon the wealth of historical, and largely unpublished information, and combine it with that most recently collected to assess the distribution and status of every regular breeding species in Dorset. To this we have added general information on the butterflies, their habitat requirements, the extent to which these habitats have changed and their prospects for the future. Extinct species and the occurrence of rare migrants are briefly described, as is the conservation of the surviving species. This is an area of growing concern; at present, the abundance and diversity of butterflies in Dorset is unmatched by any other County, but this position may be difficult to maintain.

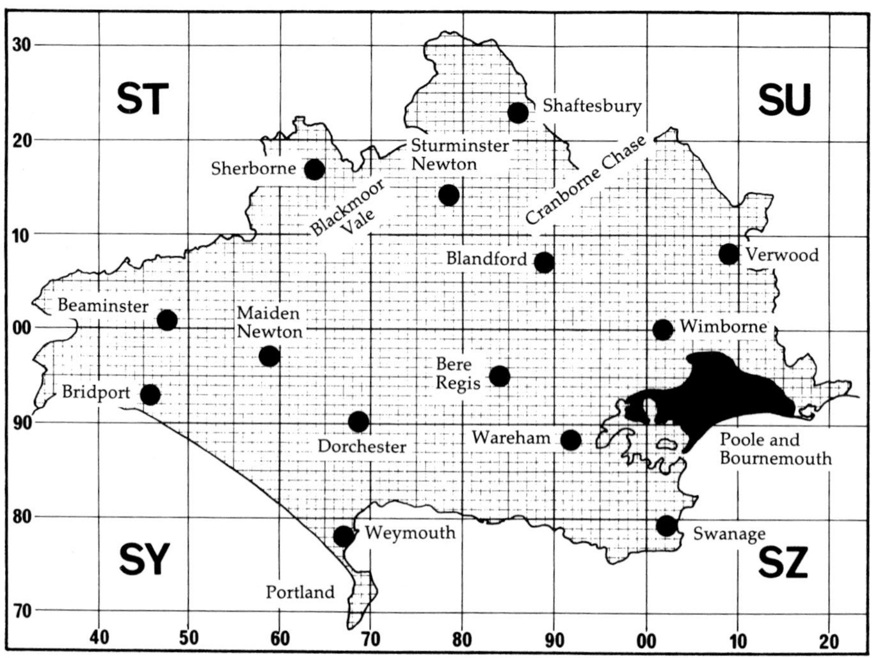

Figure 1. Main towns.

History

The first comprehensive records of butterflies in Dorset were made by James Charles Dale, Squire of Glanvilles Wootton. He was among the foremost of the English field entomologists from the first half of the 19th century, and was responsible for recording many insects new to Britain, and indeed some new to science. To us in Dorset, he is best known for his discovery of the Lulworth Skipper as a new British species in 1832. Not only was J. C. Dale an active field entomologist, but he was a noted correspondent and diarist. He maintained a compendious *Entomological Journal,* which began in 1808 when he was 17 years old, and continued until the last day of his life in 1872. This diary, his collections and his letters are now at the Hope Museum in the University of Oxford.

The Dale collection was supplemented and catalogued by his son, Charles William (1853-1907) and the *Lepidoptera of Dorsetshire* (1886) was written using the collections and journal of J. C. Dale. It also contained records from distinguished contemporaries, including the Reverend Octavius Pickard Cambridge, F.R.S., Rector of Bloxworth, a world authority on Spiders and the discoverer of the Bloxworth Blue, J. G. Ross of Bathampton, the Revd. C. R. Digby of Studland, E. R. Bankes of Corfe Castle, T. Parmiter of Kimmeridge and A. B. Farn from west Dorset. The *Lepidoptera of Dorsetshire* was disappointly brief. Dale prepared a revision which he hoped the Dorset Natural History and Antiquarian Field Club would publish, but they refused and it was published privately in 1891. Although the comments of C. W. Dale are terse, we have quoted them extensively, since they are the only general account of the status of butterflies in the County during the first half of the 19th century. However, we have not accepted his records and comments uncritically, for whereas J. C. Dale had been a meticulous and reliable worker, C. W. Dale was 'a terribly untidy man with abominable handwriting' and he introduced a number of errors into the Dorset list. Fortunately for us, these have been scrutinised by E. R. Bankes and W. Parkinson Curtis, who consulted the original writings of J. C. Dale. It is worth quoting the harsh judgements on C. W. Dale by Parkinson Curtis:

> 'I have never accepted Dale where I could get any other authority, since Dale was notoriously careless in identification and transcription of records and was exceedingly fond of adding embellishments of his own to recorded statements without distinguishing what was original and what was his own addition. I happen to know how many of the errors arose, and they arose in a way which would never have trapped a less careless person . . . Dr. A. W. Pickard Cambridge writes me: "I do not think it is in the least safe to trust to Dale's reports about Bloxworth. I went over all my father's (*the Revd. O. Pickard Cambridge*) collection with him while his memory was good, and I have a note of everything about which he was certain, and very often Dale was definitely wrong".'

On this latter point Parkinson Curtis adds, 'I knew the Revd. O. Pickard Cambridge nearly all my life and his memory was phenomenally accurate.'

In the second half of the 19th and the early years of this century, there was a number of field entomologists who between them worked the County very thoroughly, with the exception of the extreme north and the centre. The Dales explored the Blackmoor Vale from Glanvilles Wootton; A. R. Hayward worked the west and was described by Parkinson Curtis as 'the only man I know who had a really competent knowledge of west Dorset'; Nelson M. Richardson of Chickerell studied the central south; The Revd. Frank H. Fisher the north; and Dr. F. H. Haines the area around Winfrith. Purbeck and the south-east of the County were studied by F. O. Bond, E. R. Bankes, E. N. Blatchard, the Revd. O. Pickard Cambridge, W. Parkinson Curtis, and the Revd. C. D. Rigby, Rector of Studland.

Eustace Ralph Bankes of Corfe Castle was a most energetic and expert entomologist who in collaboration with the Revd. C. R. Digby, published *The Lepidoptera of the Isle of Purbeck* in Volume 6 of *The Proceedings of the Dorset Natural History and Antiquarian Field Club* in 1885. This was followed by a *First Supplement to the Lepidoptera of the Isle of Purbeck* in Volume 10 of *The Proceedings* in 1889. Throughout his life Bankes collected material and notes for a similar work which he intended should be a full account of the Lepidoptera of Dorset, but in the latter years of his life his health did not permit this work to be completed.

On the death of Bankes in 1928 all the manuscripts and materials passed into the hands of Wilfred Parkinson Curtis (1878-1968). This able and meticulous entomologist had 'started to collect seriously in 1893' and continued to acquire and sift records for the next 75 years. He knew and worked with all the late Victorian and early 20th century entomologists both within and outside the County. Like Bankes, it had been his aim to publish an account of the Lepidoptera of the County. The first step was the publication in 1934 of *A List of the Lepidoptera of Dorset* in Volume 1 of the *Transactions of the Society for British Entomology*, a society of which Parkinson Curtis had been a founder: a second part appeared in 1947 in Volume 9 of the same journal. These accounts contained introductory material and reviewed 11 families of moth, but not the butterflies; when Parkinson Curtis completed his manuscript on the latter, the Society for British Entomology refused to publish it. On his retirement in 1953, Parkinson Curtis revised and rewrote his entire list, a task which he completed just a few days before his death in 1968. The manuscript runs to 650 typed foolscap pages, but sadly, has never been published. This is deposited in the Library of the Dorset County Museum at Dorchester. A large part of the section on butterflies covers records of varieties and abberations which we have scarcely mentioned in this book.

In his accounts, Parkinson Curtis also quotes the comments of Dr. Frederick Haslefoot Haines (1864-1946) on the status of nearly every species, and we have requoted many of these. Dr. Haines was an active field entomologist in Dorset from about the turn of the century until his retirement in 1923, when he moved to the New Forest. His principal interests were flies and wasps, and he was 'an acute observer and a very complete naturalist'. He prepared a number of manuscripts on several groups of insect in the County, and although none was published, it is likely that Parkinson Curtis had access to them and that these manuscripts, together with notes from interviews are the source of many of the quotations attributed to Haines.

In addition to these private records, reports of insects, especially of Lepidoptera, appeared regularly in the *Proceedings of the Dorset Natural History and Archaeological Society*, the successor of the Field Club. These were compiled by a number of active entomologists, including A. G. B. Russell (Lancaster Herald) who became President of the Society in 1948 and devoted his Presidential Address ('*Annus mirabilis* for Butterflies and Moths') to reporting one of the most remarkable years ever for immigrant Lepidoptera, when Clouded Yellows appeared in Dorset in swarms. Other entomologists included Dr. H. King, Dr. A. A. Lisney, R. I. Lorrimer, S. C. S. Brown and A. T. Bromby.

The recent era of recording began in the early 1970s when Dr. P. Merrett began a private mapping scheme from Furzebrook Research Station. Other entomologists at the Station soon participated, and this scheme provided the basis of that adopted by the Dorset Environmental Records Centre when it was established in 1976. Field reporting has been promoted vigorously by the Centre during the last decade and a provisional atlas of the County's butterflies was published in 1980. Since then, several hundred naturalists have submitted records, both past and present, and have intensified their efforts since 1982 in response to requests for records for this book. An equal contribution has been made by staff at Furzebrook Research Station, notably in 1978, when R. W. Smith, D. J. Simcox and C. D. Thomas were employed to survey six scarce species in the County, and in 1982-84 by ourselves for this book.

The County

Forty-eight species of butterfly regularly breed in Dorset. This total includes 36 species that breed in discrete and sedentary colonies; nine mobile species that fly through the countryside and into neighbouring counties, breeding wherever suitable conditions are encountered; and three migrants – the Red Admiral, Painted Lady and Clouded Yellow – that cannot usually survive the winter, and are replenished every spring with fresh immigrants from southern Europe. In the past, there were probably another six species that were resident in the County, and in any year there is the possibility of a variety of rare migrants from abroad.

Although many butterflies are in decline in Dorset, the number of species which has become extinct is well below that of most lowland counties particularly those in the east of England. Suffolk has lost 22 species and the old County of Huntingdonshire 24. At present, we believe that no other County has as many resident species as Dorset. Our butterfly fauna is characterised by the variety and abundance of its Blues, the Lulworth Skipper and the abundance of many species that are local or moderately common elsewhere. However, the County has weaknesses in the relative dearth of woodland species and the absence of such national rarities as the Glanville and Heath Fritillaries, the Black Hairstreak and the Swallowtail.

In this section we consider those features of Dorset that are responsible for this richness: warm climate; varied geology, soils and topography; the land-use; and the range of habitats available for butterflies. We also consider how the methods of managing land have changed, particularly in recent years, with the result that many of the habitats of butterflies have been spoilt, although for one or two species conditions have improved. To explain this better we first list some general points about the habitat requirements of butterflies.

- The main factor limiting the distribution and abundance of most species is the quantity and quality of their caterpillars' foodplants. For some species, the plant may be scarce, or confined, or only certain parts of the plant may be eaten. For example, some species feed solely on tall or robust plants; others on young growth, flowers or fruits.

- The foodplant must be growing in the correct place where the microclimate meets the requirements of the eggs and caterpillars. Thus, warmth, shade and humidity must be within certain preferred limits, otherwise survival will be poor. This is more critical for some species than for others.
- The habitat requirements of many species are highly specialised. The exact locations used for breeding within a site (such as a wood) tend to be small and are different for every species.
- For the few mobile species of butterfly, there must be sufficient breeding spots to support a colony, scattered throughout the County as a whole.
- For the sedentary species (three-quarters of Dorset butterflies), suitable spots for breeding must be plentiful enough on the same site to support an entire colony year after year, or new areas must be available within their very limited range of flight.
- Once a colony of a sedentary species becomes extinct on a site, possibly because of catastrophic weather, a collector or deterioration in the quality of the habitat, it may take decades before the site is recolonised, even when ideal breeding conditions are restored, because there is no nearby source of colonists.

Climate

Almost all species of plants and animals which inhabit Britain also occur on the mainland of Europe. Most butterflies colonised these islands after the last glaciation and before the land bridge with the continent was broken. Many species migrated northwards as the climate warmed and today many of the species which occur in Britain are living at the northern limits of their world ranges. A glance at the national atlas of butterfly distribution shows that nearly half of the species are confined to the southern half of Britain and are increasingly common towards the south coast. These include many common butterflies like the Small Skipper. A few species, such as the Lulworth Skipper and Glanville Fritillary are restricted to the extreme south, where the climate is warmest. Even there breeding is confined to south-facing hills and slopes, where local conditions are hottest.

Dorset, in common with other southern counties, has a range of butterflies that is unable to survive in the cooler parts of Britain. In contrast, there are four British species that cannot survive in the south because it is too warm. Along the south coast there are other climatic differences; almost the entire County of Dorset lies within a region which has a climate intermediate between the south-east of England, where there are hot summers, cold winters and generally lower humidities, and the south-west of England, which has a more oceanic climate, with mild wet winters and cool moist summers. The central fringe of Dorset from west of Pulham to the Devon border has an oceanic climate resembling that in western Britain. It is not known whether these differences affect the survival of different butterfly species, but it is very likely. The mild winters of Dorset, during which snow is rare, probably enhance the survival of species which hibernate as adults, but on the other hand, species that hibernate in other stages of their life cycles are often more numerous after sharp winters.

It has been suggested that the recent decline of many British butterflies has been caused by a cooling of the climate. If this were so – and meterologists disagree as to whether the climate has deteriorated – one would expect the most vulnerable

Table 1. The number of species which have changed in status in Dorset compared with the national distribution of species.

National Distribution	Changes in Status of Species Increase	No Change	Decline
Throughout the UK	1	4	18
Southern half of UK	1	5	14
Extreme south of UK	1	0	0

butterflies to be species already at the northern limits of their ranges (i.e., those confined to southern Britain). Table 1 shows that no such pattern of change has occurred in Dorset. Increases in numbers, no change, and declines have been spread evenly between species that still flourish in Scotland and those that have historically been confined to the south. Indeed, the only species that is restricted to the extreme south, the Lulworth Skipper, has prospered more than any other butterfly in the County in recent years. This is because its habitat has dramatically improved: we attribute most changes in the status of butterflies in Dorset to habitat changes.

This is not to say that variation in the weather from one year to the next does not have a considerable effect by causing short term fluctuations in butterfly numbers. Prolonged cold, wet weather in the spring and summer can result in fewer eggs being laid and the reduced survival of young stages. Extreme drought and heat can be even more harmful, especially on thin soils or south facing slopes, when many larval foodplants die back. There were declines in the numbers of several species during and after the hot, dry summer of 1976, and some colonies that were already very small through breeding in poor habitats became extinct. We illustrate the severe decline experienced by the Adonis Blue on a down near Swanage in 1976 (Figure 2). In this case, the colony was large enough to survive this drought and to increase rapidly into its vacant habitat in 1977-80, even though the spring and summer temperatures were lower than usual. After three years, recovery was complete and the colony settled down to more typical annual fluctuations. By and large, any local increase or decrease caused by weather is temporary.

Geology

The topography of the County is dominated by the central outcrop of chalk and other Cretaceous deposits, which cross it from north-east to south-west. To the east of the chalk lie younger Tertiary deposits which are the westernmost part of the Hampshire Basin: the so-called Poole Basin. To the north and west of the chalk escarpment are a series of older Jurassic and Liassic rocks with strata of varying complexity.

The central chalk escarpment is a south-western extension of the large area of chalk which forms Salisbury Plain. This outcrop is widest at the point where it enters the County, high on Cranborne Chase. It tapers south-westwards to a location just to the north of Abbotsbury, from which branches run north-westwards almost to reach the Somerset border north of Beaminster and eastwards to the coast between Arish Mell and Worbarrow Bay, whence a thin ridge runs eastwards as the Purbeck Hills. This ridge terminates in Ballard Down and the Foreland (Old Harry Rocks) but until early Quaternary times was continuous with the chalk on the Isle of Wight, connecting with the Needles. The escarpment of the chalk is marked by such high points as Melbury Down, Bulbarrow, Batcombe Hill and Black Down. The highest point on the chalk of Purbeck is Nine Barrow Down. All these places have elevations which are between approximately 200 and 275 metres. In several places there are deposits of clay-with-flints lying over the chalk; these are mainly towards the higher points of the escarpment.

The dip slope of the chalk falls gently eastwards to form a basin which is overlain with Tertiary deposits; these commence to the east of Dorchester, in the vicinity of Warmwell and Higher Woodford, and in the south run parallel to the ridge of the Purbeck Hills until Studland. North-eastwards these deposits pass Bloxworth and Wimborne to Cranborne. These Tertiary deposits are almost entirely Bagshot Sands, with seams of pipe-clay and varying amounts of plateau gravels. The river valleys are bounded by alluvial deposits and valley gravels. Poole Harbour was formed in post-glacial times about 6,000 years ago, when the sea-level rose and

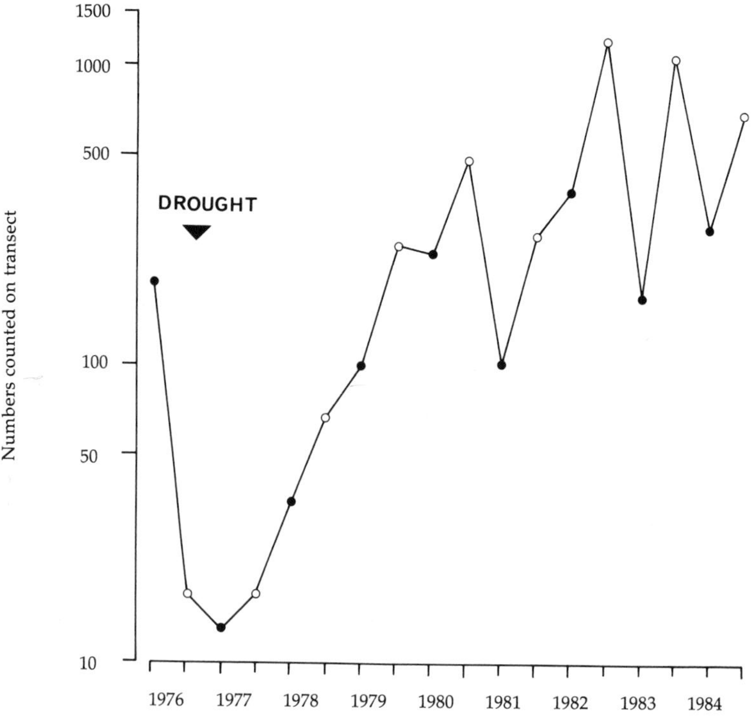

Figure 2. Changes in numbers of Adonis Blue at a site near Swanage. ● *spring brood;* ○ *summer brood.*

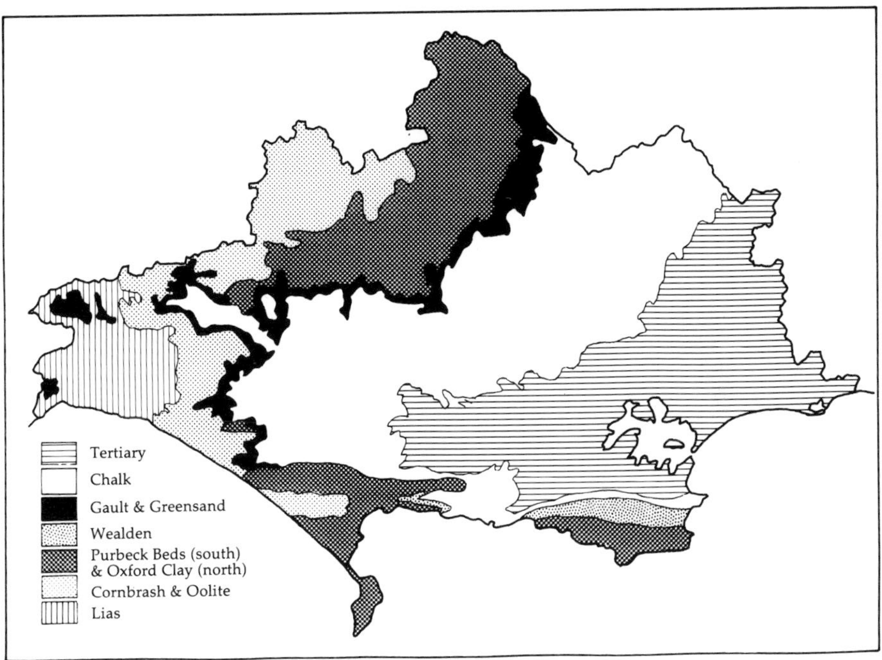

Figure 3. A simplified geological map of Dorset.

flooded the lowest parts of the Tertiary basin. The islands in Poole Harbour correspond to the knolls which are a feature of the heathland landscape.

Northwards and westwards of the chalk escarpment the series of outcrops is much more complex and projections from the main body of chalk form a series of vales. In the north-west, the chalk is bounded by a series of strata representing Greensand, Gault, Kimmeridge Clay, Corallian Limestone and Oxford Clays. The outermost deposits are of Oolites, Cornbrash with Forest Marble and Fullers Earth. South of the chalk, to the west of Weymouth, are Greensands, Gault, Corallian Limestones and Oxford Clays. Portland consists of Portland Limestone with a northern peripheral band of Kimmeridge Clay. To the south of the chalk in Purbeck are very narrow bands of Greensand and Gault, a wider band of Wealden Clays and a ridge of Portland and Purbeck Limestones with a coastal fringe of Kimmeridge Clay. West of the chalk, in the Marshwood Vale and beyond, there are further, wider outcrops of Greensands and Gault, Oolites and Cornbrash. The remaining area to the County border consists of a series of Liassic deposits. The complexity of the deposits to the north and west of the chalk are the cause of the varied landscape of vales and the diversity of the vegetation in this region.

Professor R. Good, in his *Geographical Handbook of the Dorset Flora* (1948) divided the County into a number of biological regions based mainly on the river systems and the underlying geology. For our purposes it is not necessary to use the detail of Professor Good's regions, and if the reader requires a fuller account he should consult the *Geographical Handbook.* Suffice it to say that the chalk is conveniently divided by the Rivers Stour and Frome into the northern, central and southern chalk. To the north-east, the Blackmoor and Halstock Vales are the main clay vales, while in the west there is a group of smaller vales dominated by the Marshwood Vale. South of the chalk and west from Weymouth, lies another distinct vale. The Isles of Portland and Purbeck form well defined units, as do the Tertiary soils around Poole Harbour, which we, like Good, will call the Poole Basin.

Soils

Each of the main geological formations gives rise to distinctive types of soil on which the vegetational diversity (and hence that of the butterflies) of the County depends. In the whole of the Tertiary Poole Basin, the podsol is the main soil type. These are well drained sandy, acidic soils with a distinct pan layer which forms at varying depths, because of the redeposition of iron and humus leached from the upper layers of the soil by rainfall. This effect further impoverishes what are already very poor soils. In places where the drainage is impeded by clay layers or there is a persistently high water table, a modification, the gleyed podsol, forms. These Tertiary soils are very poor and acidic (pH 3-4). They support a characteristic vegetation of dwarf shrubs with few associated species and have a small but distinct range of butterflies. Bordering the main areas of podsols are Brown earths, which also occur in parts of the north and west of the County. These are coarse to fine loamy soils. Where there is more clay, the drainage may be impeded.

The soils of the chalk lands are rendzinas – thin, well-drained soils in which the parent material is often close to the surface. In some places, there may be flinty layers of drift. All these soils are highly calcareous and support a variety of plants that is unmatched on other soils. Many of these are the foodplants of butterflies, and in some cases grow nowhere else.

The soils in the vales of the north and west of the County are surface and groundwater gleys, and are associated with Jurassic rocks. These are well structured soils with both mineral particles and loam, and drainage is generally good. In parts where the proportion of clay is higher, drainage becomes increasingly impeded and causes reducing conditions where there may be veins of iron. Despite this many of these soils in the northern and western vales support a good deal of livestock farming and form a distinct biological region of the County.

This is only an outline of the soil types, the detailed picture is much more complex and the reader is referred to the recent maps produced by the Soil Survey of England and Wales. Nevertheless, the distributions of many butterfly species can be related to this simplified pattern as shown in Figure 3. An older but more comprehensive account of the soils of Dorset was written for the *Geographical Handbook of the Dorset Flora* by K. L. Robinson.

Woodlands

Because most of its soils are well drained, and were easily cleared and cultivated, Dorset now has a modest area of woodland compared with neighbouring counties. Extensive tracts exist only on Cranborne Chase and in the modern plantations on the Tertiary soils: elsewhere woods tend to be small and isolated but are well distributed on all soils throughout the County (Figure 4: taken from *The Dorset Woodlands—Their History and Conservation* (1976) by M. S. Warren). As a consequence, Dorset has never been noted for its woodland butterflies. Although the species list is impressive, colonies are comparatively few, especially of insects that prefer extensively wooded regions and heavy soils, for example the Brown Hairstreak and Purple Emperor. Yet despite this, the woods of Dorset are far from negligible, and places such as Powerstock Common, Brackett's Coppice, Deadmoor Common and Cranborne Chase are nationally important for their butterflies. At least 38 species of butterfly still breed regularly in Dorset woods. Admittedly, most of these are more numerous in unwooded places, but there are at least 13 species that depend largely or wholly on woods for their survival.

The area of woodland in Dorset has changed dramatically over the ages and was at an all-time-low around 1808 when J. C. Dale began his *Entomological Journal,* following the centuries of clearance which culminated in a desperate need for timber during the Napoleonic Wars. Since then the area of woodland has doubled

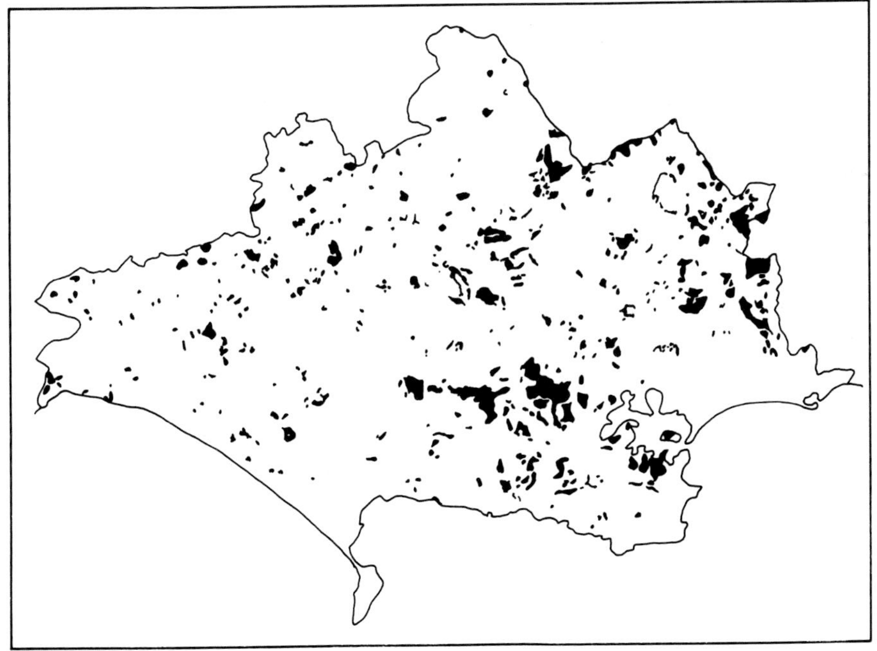

Figure 4. The larger woods of Dorset (after M. S. Warren).

to its present total of about 23,000 hectares (Figure 5). However, most of the new woods are uninteresting and are mainly dense conifer plantations on former heathland with its impoverished ground flora. Nevertheless it is extremely disappointing that there has been no equivalent increase in woodland butterflies during the last 175 years. Only three species – the Comma, Speckled Wood and White Admiral – have spread in woods during this century, and to some extent this represents a recolonisation of old localities from which these species had mysteriously disappeared in the mid and late 19th century. However, the Speckled Wood and White Admiral now greatly exceed their former abundance. On the debit side, and considering only true woodland butterflies, the Black-veined White and Large Tortoiseshell became extinct during this period, and another six species have declined alarmingly and are close to extinction in the County.

The severe decline of the White-letter Hairstreak was caused by the effects of Dutch elm disease, but the clue to most, if not all, other changes in the abundance of butterflies lies in the manner in which the woods of the County are now managed. Each of the 38 species that breed in woods requires its own particular habitat: to generalise, 29 species breed amongst the ground flora, seven species use shrubs and only two species (White-letter Hairstreak and Purple Hairstreak) breed

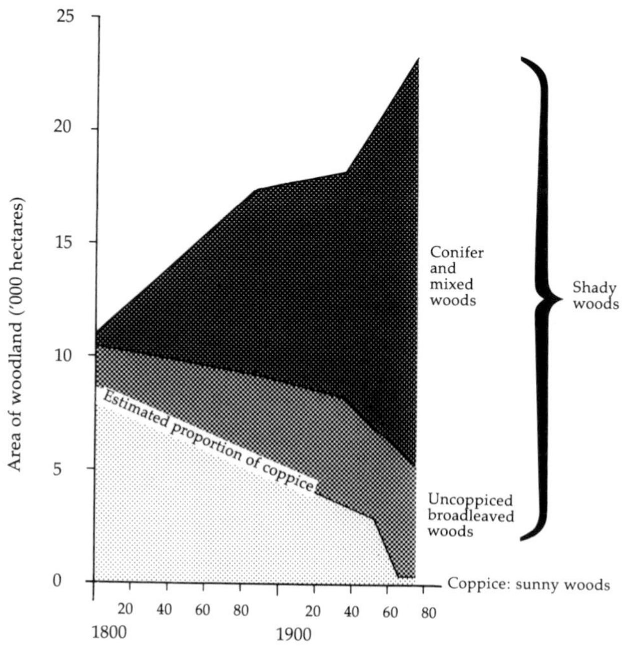

Figure 5. Changes in the area and composition of woods in Dorset 1810-1972 (from M. S. Warren, 1976 and personal communication). Estimates of coppice before 1906 are by M. S. Warren.

on the trees themselves. Traditionally, most of the woods in the County were managed as Hazel coppice, often with Oaks as standard trees. The coppice was cut in small patches or blocks every eight to fifteen years to provide a supply of poles, thatching spars and hurdles. The Oaks were felled for timber when it was required and usually long before the canopy had closed, so that about 60 per cent of the sunlight still reached the ground. As a result, a continuum was maintained for many centuries of habitats that were very open and sunny, yet sheltered. Freshly cut coppices were famous for their rich ground flora, especially those on the chalk. Good examples, with a profusion of Bugle, Violets, Vetches, Trefoils, Strawberries and Primroses, can still be seen after the cutting in the small fragments of worked coppice that remain around Bloxworth, Milborne St. Andrew, Dorchester and on Cranborne Chase. Such clearings once provided numerous breeding sites for High Brown, Pearl-bordered and Small Pearl-bordered Fritillaries, Wood White, Duke of Burgundy, Small Copper, Grizzled and Dingy Skippers, and Common Blue. All were common or abundant in early Victorian coppices but have gradually declined as the call for coppice products diminished and many woods were abandoned. Nevertheless, nearly half of the ancient woods in the County were still coppiced in the late 1940s, but in the next ten years coppicing dropped to a negligible area. The coppices and their standards were left to grow up into dense, shady woods; any new woods were plantations, which in their turn became too shady. At present, roughly 2 per cent of woodland in the County contains the sunny open conditions that are essential for most of the traditional species of woodland butterflies, and the remaining 98 per cent of woodlands are shadier than they have been for a thousand years or more (Figure 5). Moreover, the loss of rabbits in the 1950s must have led to additional shading of the ground flora. In view of this, it is not surprising that most sun-loving species have declined. Those surviving are sadly diminished and exist as isolated relicts, facing extinction in the County.

The story is not wholly of losses. Both the White Admiral and Speckled Wood need quite shady conditions and have been spreading continuously since about 1910 into what, for them, is an improved habitat. Moreover, the Browns and those Skippers that prefer tall, sheltered grass, are extremely abundant in most woods; much more so than on their traditional grassland localities in several regions where farming has been intensified. For the same reason, woods have become islands where species, such as the Orange Tip, can breed in some parts of the County. Thus, apart from the Speckled Wood and White Admiral, one is much more likely to see the so-called hedgerow and grassland species in the woodlands of Dorset, than the traditional woodland butterflies. Other exceptions are the Silver-washed Fritillary, which prefers slightly shadier conditions than the other Fritillaries and is still locally common, and the Purple Hairstreak, which has survived well, often on isolated oaks next to large conifer plantations.

Grasslands and Downlands

A high percentage of Dorset consists of fields, downs and hedgerows. These open areas were created by man through primeval forest clearances and most have been farmed in various ways and at fluctuating intensities ever since. Even under today's intensive farming, two thirds of the species of butterfly are more numerous on open or unwooded land than on wooded. Species such as these, and especially those traditionally associated with open grasslands, must have benefitted enormously from the ancient forest clearances. Before Neolithic times, it is believed that these species were confined to temporary woodland clearings, the open conditions on steep slopes and thin or poor soils, and especially, on the eroding coasts.

The richest grasslands for butterflies are the chalk and limestone downs and hills. This is mainly due to their diverse flora; the foodplants of the Adonis Blue, Chalkhill Blue, Small Blue, Brown Argus, Lulworth Skipper and Silver-spotted Skipper grow mostly on these calcareous soils and those of many other butterflies are abundant. In addition, the microtopography of many spots along the steep escarpments provides unusually warm microclimates and ideal breeding places for species which are adapted to the warmer conditions of central southern Europe.

Over the centuries, the way in which the land of Dorset has been farmed has changed continuously. The main influences have been the prevailing economic forces, changing tastes, the Enclosures Acts, population changes, the special demands of wars, and the development of chemical techniques, new varieties of seeds and mechanisation. Such factors have greatly affected the balance and size of colonies of the different species of butterfly during the present century and this has almost certainly always been the case. In the Napoleonic Wars, the extent of arable land was perhaps the greatest it has ever been, and these areas would have

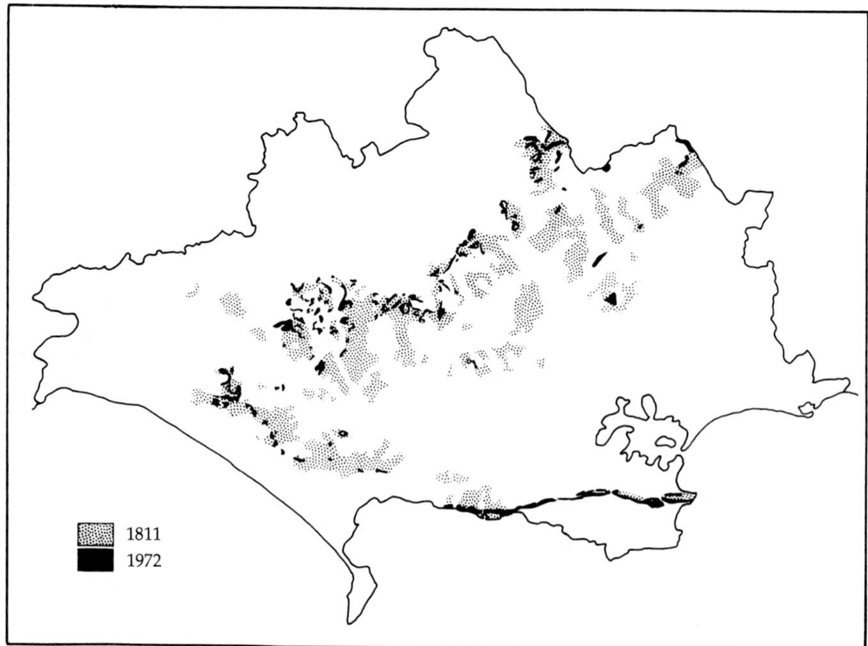

Figure 6. The decline of semi-natural chalk grassland in Dorset, 1811-1972 (after C. A. Jones, 1973). Note that limestone grassland is not shown.

1 Lulworth Skipper females

2 Lulworth Skipper male

3 Small Skipper

4 Essex Skipper

5 Silver-spotted Skipper

6 Large Skipper

7 Dingy Skipper

8 Grizzled Skipper

9 Clouded Yellow

10 Brimstone

11 Small White

12 Green-veined White

13 Orange Tip male

14 Orange Tip female

15 Large White

16 Orange Tip male

17 Wood White

18 Small Copper

19 White-letter Hairstreak

20 Green Hairstreak

21 Brown Hairstreak

22 Purple Hairstreak

23 Chalkhill Blue male

24 Adonis Blue female

25 Brown Argus

26 Adonis Blue male

27 Holly Blue
28 Small Blue
29 Silver-studded Blue
30 Silver-studded Blue
31 Common Blue
32 Duke of Burgundy

33 Purple Emperor

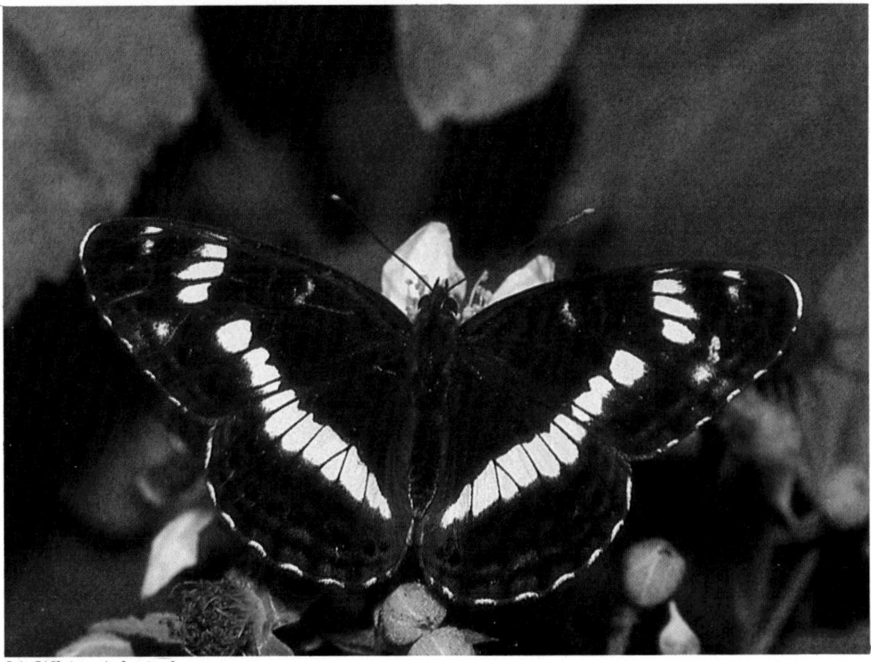

34 White Admiral

35 Comma

36 Comma

37 Small Tortoiseshell

38 Red Admiral

39 Painted Lady

40 Peacock

41 Small Pearl-bordered Fritillary

42 Small Pearl-bordered Fritillary

43 Pearl-bordered Fritillary

44 Pearl-bordered Fritillary

45 High Brown Fritillary

46 Dark-green Fritillary

47 Marsh Fritillary

48 Silver-washed Fritillary

49 Meadow Brown

50 Small Heath

51 Gatekeeper

52 Speckled Wood

53 Wall

54 Marbled White

55 Ringlet

56 Grayling

provided breeding grounds for a few butterflies dependant on weeds, such as the Small Copper, but for very few others. Much land was abandoned after the Black Death, and similarly, during the great agricultural depression in the late 19th century. At these times, it is likely that those species of Browns and Skippers that both feed on grasses and thrive in tall swards were more abundant. On the other hand, there was probably a corresponding reduction in the numbers of species such as Small Copper, Grayling, Dingy Skipper, Grizzled Skipper, Silver-spotted Skipper and most Blues, all of which flourish in open or short swards. The heyday of these latter species was probably during the 17th century when, at the height of the wool trade, it is estimated that the sheep flocks of Dorset totalled ten million animals. By the mid 18th century this number had dwindled to 800,000. Despite this, short open grassland remained the dominant habitat, so much so that in 1793, J. Claridge wrote:

> 'The most striking feature of the County is the open and unenclosed parts, covered by numerous flocks of sheep, scattered over the Downs, which are in general of a delightful verdure and smoothness affording a scene beautifully picturesque.'

At first sight this scene exists today, but most of the sheep have gone and, beautiful as the rolling downs appear, they have been horribly changed for butterflies.

There are two changes that have affected butterflies; the majority of fields has been improved by draining, ploughing, dressing with fertilisers, reseeding and the application of herbicides. Through these operations, most of the native herbs and grasses have been eliminated and replaced by a few species, cultivars or exotics. The yield from the land has increased but the populations of butterflies have declined.

The flatter areas of the County are those which have been altered most by intensive farming. No figure is available for the losses of semi-natural communities in Dorset, but in the old County of Huntingdon no more than 0.4 per cent of land on the flat clays survives as flower-rich, natural grasslands, and the same is probably true here. The chalklands have been surveyed in more detail and in 1970 about 3.5 per cent had survived improvement. The map (Figure 6, taken from *The Conservation of Chalk Dowland in Dorset* (1973) by C. A. Jones) shows the estimated losses between 1811 and 1972. It should be noted that the surviving fragments consist of sites situated almost entirely along the escarpment from Melbury Down in the north-east, extending south-westwards through Hod Hill, Bulbarrow and Bingham's Melcombe to Cerne Abbas, Sydling St. Nicholas and Cattistock, thence to Eggardon Hill and Litton Cheney, and finally south-eastwards, via Bincombe, Lulworth and Corfe Castle to Swanage. Many maps of the distributions of butterflies in this book clearly show this pattern. These hills have survived intensive cultivation, mainly because of their steepness and their thin soils. This is one reason why Dorset retains a variety of species that has been eliminated from the flatter counties. Moreover, these steep slopes happen always to have been among the best areas for butterflies because of their thin soils, sparse swards and their warm micro-climates. Although there have been considerable losses of the commoner and of some local species of butterflies on the flatter downland, it is unlikely that flat areas ever supported many colonies of the scarce species, such as the Adonis Blue and Silver-spotted Skipper.

The other major change during this century has been the change in the character of the few surviving fragments of semi-natural grasslands. For most of this century there has been a drift towards abandoning the steep, unproductive hills, as was already the case in the late 19th century. However, most were prevented from becoming overgrown by rabbit grazing which produced a sward like a billiard table. These formed the preferred habitats of the Adonis Blue, a few other Blues and the Silver-spotted Skipper, but most other species were scarce. With the death of rabbits from myxomatosis in the 1950s, there was a short period when the downs flowered, and many species of butterfly became abundant. Subsequently, tall, dense swards of Tor Grass (*Brachypodium pinnatum*), and in the north of the County, Upright Brome Grass (*Bromus errectus*) grew up. This was followed by an encroachment of scrub on to the open downland; in the south mostly of Gorse and in the north mostly of Hawthorn. These changes provided ideal conditions for several species of Browns and Skippers, although this by no means compensated for the huge losses that had occurred on the flatter lands. However, in the case of the Lulworth Skipper, which had always been restricted to warm, overgrown hills, the increase was absolute, and populations grew to hundreds of thousands of individuals on the coastal hills of Purbeck. On the other hand, there were widespread extinctions of colonies of Adonis Blue, Grayling, Silver-spotted Skipper and Silver-studded Blue. Many of the other species which depend on fairly short or sparse swards also became scarcer.

This trend became most acute in the late 1970s and by 1978 only 58 per cent of the unimproved, calcareous grasslands in Dorset was being grazed. Even when there was grazing, stocking rates were often too light or too erratic to generate suitable conditions for the short-grass species. Four-fifths of the sites had a sward that was taller than 10 centimetres when surveyed in 1978. Since that time conditions have altered; rabbits have returned and the numbers of sheep grazing the downs has increased. By the early 1980s, many of the swards were again short (but less herb-rich than formerly) and on some sites the huge populations of Lulworth Skipper had decreased, whereas the Adonis Blue and related species had increased and begun to recolonise adjacent areas. This situation is unlikely to last for long as grazing has again begun to decline due to economic factors.

Hedgerows

Although the hedgerows, hedge banks and verges of the County support populations of a wide range of species that need shrubs or shelter for breeding the grassland species amongst this number are rather few. The ground flora beneath the hedges has become overgrown or dominated by tall grasses, and although this has been to the benefit of some butterflies, it has been to the detriment of others. Limited as the range may be, hedgerows and banks are often the only places where butterflies can breed today outside of the woods in the flatter parts of the County.

Coastlands

The Dorset coastline consists of a diverse range of outcrops and soils. It supports a strip of semi-natural vegetation that has scarcely been affected by farming. Although the loss of rabbits has caused many areas to become overgrown, many other areas are unstable and new habitats are constantly being created. The thin soils and sparse swards, with low growing herbs intermixed between clumps of tall grass are an important habitat for a wide range of 'short' and 'tall grass' species. Moreover, the entire coastline faces south and is consequently hot, providing better conditions for most species and rare breeding sites for those that need very warm conditions. The prospects for many areas of the coastline are good since they are now owned and managed by the National Trust.

Heathlands

The heathlands, which stretch from near Dorchester eastwards to the Hampshire border and encircle Poole Harbour, are one of the most famous features of the Dorset landscape. Contrary to popular belief, these sandy, barren wastes clothed with purple heather, are not primeval, but have been shaped by the activities of men over many centuries. Heathland vegetation, dominated by dwarf ericaceous shrubs, spread after the thin deciduous forests were cleared by Bronze Age men about 3,600 years ago. When the tree cover had been removed, these poor acid soils deteriorated further and hindered the regeneration of the forest and, more importantly, grazing by domestic animals also prevented regeneration. It is thought that in Dorset, heathland was well established on all the Tertiary soils in the Poole Basin by Roman times. It remained so until the middle of the 18th century and throughout this time was kept open by grazing, turf cutting, the gathering of 'furze and fern' (gorse and bracken) and probably by periodic fires. We cannot be certain about the role played by fire and it may be that this form of management, which temporarily improved the quality of the grazing, may have been introduced from the uplands where it became a standard practice for managing sheep moors after the 18th century.

After the middle of the 18th century century, agricultural methods improved and it was possible, by dressing with lime and fertiliser, to take heathland into cultivation, a process which has continued until the present times. From the late 19th century, afforestation began to occur and many other areas of heathland were taken. The expansion of Poole and Bournemouth (which did not exist until the mid-19th century) has also been onto heathland.

In the middle of the 18th century almost all the area of the Tertiary soils was covered in heathland, some 40,000 hectares. Today, just under 6,000 ha remain (Figure 7) and much of that which survives is in small isolated fragments. Not only have the heathlands decreased in extent but the traditional uses have ceased. Only in one or two places is there grazing; today the main checks on the regeneration of woodland are the all too frequent fires. It is important to realise that without some check on the growth of scrub and trees the open heathland would not exist and in this respect fire is a useful agent now that the other practices have ceased.

The range of plants found on the heathlands is rather poor compared with downland and woodland. Likewise there are only two butterflies which are really characteristic of the Dorset heath today, the Grayling and the Silver-studded Blue. The Grayling is a species of sandy, or gravelly open spaces and it also occurs on dry open stony soils on the downlands. It has become much scarcer on the downlands and our surviving heath are now its stronghold. The Silver-studded Blue is much more of a heathland species, and makes use of some typically heathland plants for food. It relies on the creation of early successional stages of vegetation such as would have been generated in the past by turf cutting and periodic burning. It lives in discrete colonies and the fragmentation and isolation which has affected the heath now means that many populations are very isolated. If they die out they are unlikely to be recolonised from other distant sites. The heathlands of Dorset and the New Forest are the stronghold of this species in Britain.

We may speculate that in the past the use of the heathlands created more diverse conditions; grazing and cutting may have resulted in more fine-leaved grasses being present in the vegetation. This would have benefited species such as the Small Heath, which is now largely confined to the remaining grassy patches. The marginal areas of the heathlands, particularly where dominated by bracken are still a common locality for the Gatekeeper, and the damper scrubby parts with suitable foodplants have small populations of Brimstone. Throughout the heath areas Gorse flourishes on boundary banks and disturbed ground which creates ideal conditions for the Green Hairstreak and it can frequently be seen in this habitat.

In addition many of the roads and some narrow gauge railways for hauling clay have been built on chalk foundations, which causes strips of calcareous vegetation across the heaths. Species such as the Marbled White and Brown Argus may occur here and more remarkably, in one locality there is a colony of the Lulworth Skipper. Finally, as with all habitats, mobile species of butterfly can be seen from time to time on the heathlands.

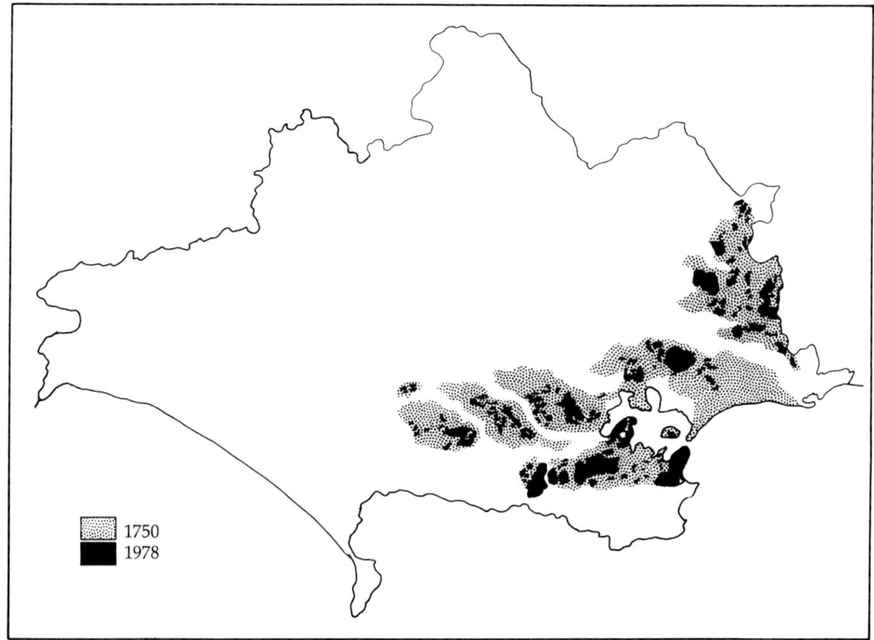

Figure 7. The decline of heathland in Dorset, 1759-1978 (after N. R. Webb and L. E. Haskins, 1980).

Dorset Butterflies

In this section we attempt to describe the requirements of every species that regularly breeds in the County, and to summarise the past and present distribution and status of each. There are 48 species, including the three commonest migrants; the Red Admiral, Painted Lady and Clouded Yellow. Every species is treated separately except for the Essex and Small Skippers, which are combined because our knowledge of the former in the County is poor. Finally, extinct species, rare migrants and accidental species are considered.

The Maps

Figure 8 is a map which indicates the extent of recording since 1970. It has been compiled by shading all 1 km squares from which at least one record has been received for any species. For each species, the maps summarise both past and present distributions and largely replace the long lists of localities which formed the bulk of the writings of Dale and Parkinson Curtis. Records are plotted as the

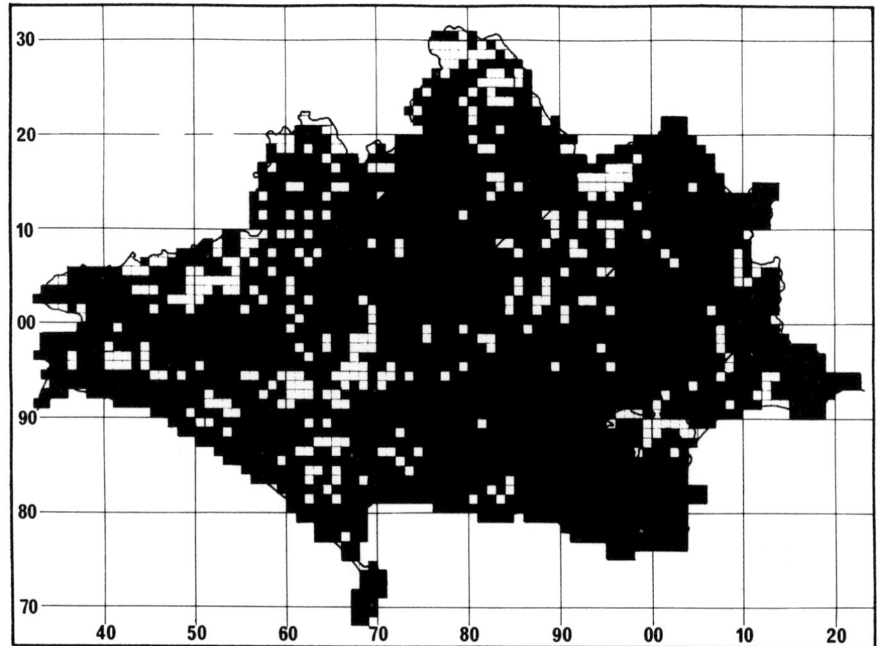

Figure 8. The coverage achieved by the recent recording scheme. For every closed square there has been at least one record submitted.

presence or absence of a species in the 2613 different 1 km squares from the Ordnance Survey National Grid which covers the County. They have been divided into four date classes, each with a different symbol

pre 1900	▣
1900-1939	⧄
1940-1969	◪
1970-1984	■

Where records from two date classes coincide, only the most recent has been plotted. This method has the disadvantage of masking the former distributions of a few species, such as the Comma, that have spread in recent years. Where this has occurred we have commented in the text. The majority of the records in the most recent date class were collected between 1978 and 1984.

The post 1969 category of records is much more comprehensive than any of the older ones for several reasons; modern entomologists are more mobile, thanks to the car; there are fewer places to search in Dorset because of modern farming methods; and many of the old records are too imprecise to map at a scale of 1 km square. In addition, the old entomologists, including Parkinson Curtis, did not bother to list localities of species which they considered to be common. This is very tantalising since several, such as the Pearl-bordered Fritillary, are now extremely rare.

The maps were drawn by the Dorset Environmental Records Centre, mainly from the sources already described, including the manuscript of Parkinson Curtis. In addition, records of common species have been added from the national recording scheme organised by the Biological Records Centre of the Institute of Terrestrial Ecology. It has been a considerable achievement by the Dorset Environmental Records Centre to obtain such comprehensive records. We are convinced that the maps are meaningful and do not represent merely the distribution of recorders. However, with a few exceptions, they are not definitive, and the following points should be borne in mind:

- Most maps are incomplete. A glance at those for the ubiquitous Small Tortoiseshell, Large and Small Whites shows that certain regions, such as north-west Dorset have been more poorly covered than others.

- Certain species have been less well surveyed than others, often because they are comparatively drab such as the Skippers, or elusive such as the woodland Hairstreaks. And in general, rare and local species have been much better mapped than the common ones, which have frequently been ignored. Moreover, there have been special surveys of seven local species: Small Blue, Adonis Blue, Purple Emperor, Lulworth Skipper (all in 1978), Silver-spotted Skipper (1978 and 1982), Marsh Fritillary (1978 and 1983) and Duke of Burgundy (1984).

- The maps undoubtedly contain a small number of errors or misleading records. Genuine, but misleading records are obtained for a few species, like the Marsh Fritillary, that occasionally stray from their discrete colonies. Errors may occur through mis-identifications or faulty recording of grid references.

Together with the Records Centre, we have attempted to check as many strange records as possible. In addition, about 25 copies of provisional maps were distributed to experts throughout the County in 1983 and 1984 for comments and checking of localities. It is possible that a few genuine records have inadvertantly been rejected, for which we apologise. A few omissions may have been caused by the lengthy process of drawing the maps.

Adult Flight Periods

Histograms have been provided to show the adult flight periods of all but five species. These have been compiled from the regular counts of butterflies that have been made along fixed transects in Dorset, some as part of the national Butterfly Monitoring Scheme. We have used data from transects at Swanage (1976-1983 by J. A. Thomas, P. Merrett, L. Clemence and others), Studland (1976-1983 by J. R. Cox), Fontmell Down (1981-1983 by W. G. Shreeves and C. J. Tubb), Stubhampton Bottom (1980-1983 by C. J. Tubb) and Hod Hill (1983-1984 by C. J. Tubb). At each place the transect route is a mile or more in length, and has been walked once a week each year from 1st April until 30th September. We have combined the counts obtained in all years to produce an overall picture of the probabilities of seeing each species in any week. It should be borne in mind that a few species fly earlier or later than the recording period, and where this is so, we have commented. Moreover, the peak emergence may vary by a week or two from year to year, depending on the warmth of the season. Thus the combined flight periods, made over 9 years, show slightly longer adult periods than are likely to occur in any particular year.

The Texts

In the texts we explain the requirements of each species, inasmuch as these are known, and describe the places where each species can be found. We also comment on the maps and quote extensively from the writings of C. W. Dale and W. Parkinson Curtis. Where changes in status have occurred, we describe or speculate on their likely causes.

The Illustrations

Each species is illustrated in colour. The aim is to give the reader an impression of the range of butterflies that can be seen in the Dorset countryside. It has not been our intention to produce a handbook for identification. Although many species can be readily identified from these plates, many others, such as some Blues, Fritillaries and Skippers cannot. Identification may depend on characters not shown in the plates, or there may be differences in the markings of each sex. We refer readers to two handbooks – both by Dorset residents

British Butterflies by Robert Goodden (David & Charles 1978)

A Complete Guide to British Butterflies by Margaret Brooks and Charles Knight (Jonathan Cape, 1982).

SMALL SKIPPER – *Thymelicus sylvestris* Plate 3
ESSEX SKIPPER – *Thymelicus lineola* Plate 4

The adults of these two Skippers are almost identical and differ principally in the colour of the undersides of the clubs of the antennae; on the Small Skipper this is orange whereas on the Essex Skipper it is black. The black bar on the upper forewing of the Essex Skipper is fractionally longer than in the Small Skipper and is less pronounced. Contrary to popular opinion, the Essex Skipper is not confined to its named county and since both species often fly together, most naturalists fail to separate them. There is little doubt that the Essex Skipper occurs in Dorset, but like Parkinson Curtis and other entomologists, we have failed to find it, although sufficient specimens have been examined to conclude that the majority of sightings in Dorset are of Small Skippers.

The natural history of the two species is different. The Essex Skipper hibernates in the egg and the Small Skipper, which hatches in the summer, as a caterpillar. The former lays its eggs on Creeping Soft Grass (*Holcus mollis*), Cocksfoot (*Dactylis glomerata*) or, in some areas, on Timothy (*Phleum pratense*); the Small Skipper almost always uses Yorkshire Fog Grass (*H. lanatus*). Both species lay their eggs on mature, tall plants and colonies are found where these wild grasses remain and are allowed to grow tall. Small strips of land, such as verges and hedge banks may support colonies, and huge numbers develop an abandoned pasture, cliffs, undercliffs and in woodland rides and glades.

Distribution and Status

Small Skipper: In the 19th century Dale described it as 'generally distributed', and Parkinson Curtis thought it was 'common in all districts' upto the 1960s. Today, the Small Skipper is a common butterfly in semi-natural vegetation throughout the County, although on the heathlands it is confined to the grassy sides of tracks. It is rare on closely cropped fields and absent from all improved grasslands. Both species must now be much less common because of changes in the farmland on the flatter areas of chalk and clay. However, as with most grass feeding species, surviving colonies have probably increased on the remaining fragments. The map underestimates the present distribution of the Small Skipper in Dorset, since it is often ignored by recorders.

Essex Skipper: This species is undoubtedly rare and local in Dorset. There are 26 reports, of which all but five are from Purbeck and the coast westwards to Portland. All sightings are from chalk or limestone grasslands. The first authentic record was for Swanage in 1928, but we have failed to find it here, despite many checks.

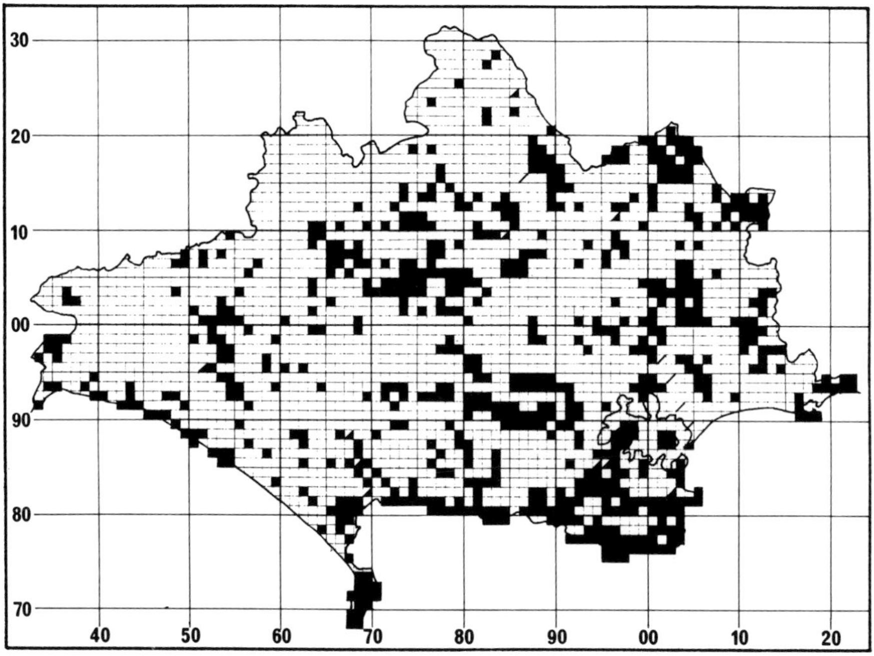

Where to see: The Small Skipper can be seen in rough places in open grassland, woods, verges, cliffs and undercliffs where Yorkshire Fog Grass grows in tall clumps.

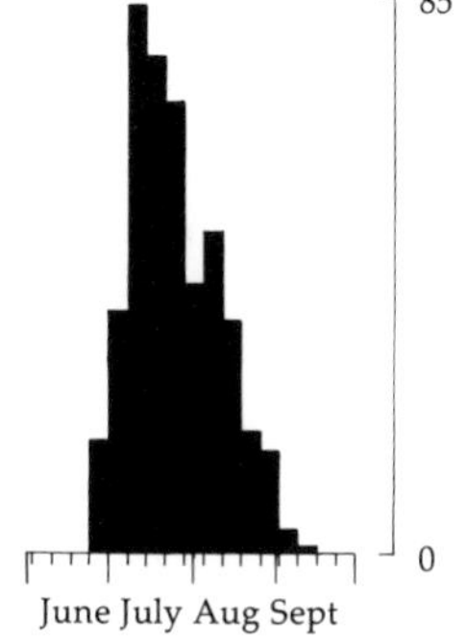

When to see: The histogram is from Ballard Down and is constructed from sightings of the Small Skipper. The Essex Skipper flies about one week later, although generally both species coincide.

LULWORTH SKIPPER – *Thymelicus acteon* Plates 1 and 2

The Lulworth Skipper is one of the specialities of Dorset; indeed nearly all the British colonies of this butterfly occur within the County. It was first discovered at Durdle Door in 1832 by J. C. Dale, and was soon found at several places along the coastline between Weymouth and Swanage. These colonies still survive and it is most heartening that, at a time when most species of butterfly are decreasing in abundance, this attractive Skipper is prospering and increasing. Today it can be seen in vast numbers almost continuously along the south-east coast in July and August. The tiny males are dun coloured, almost olive-green, but with far less orange than the Small Skipper, which although similar is slightly larger. The females are chequered, like a very small Silver-spotted or Large Skipper. Adult Lulworth Skippers rarely leave their discrete colonies: these occur only on calcareous soils, with three apparent exceptions on chalk embankments laid for railways across the heathlands and clays of Purbeck.

Like all Skippers, the adults rest during overcast weather, but in sunshine they are extremely active, monopolising flowers of Marjoram, Bird's-foot Trefoil and thistles. The eggs are laid within the sheaths of tall, mature clumps of Tor Grass (*Brachypodium pinnatum*). The newly-hatched caterpillar hibernates in a silken web spun within the sheath. It does not feed until the following spring, when it ascends the leaves at night, making characteristic V-shaped notches in the blade. When older, it draws the blade around itself with silk cords and eats all of the leaf except the mid-rib and its silk tube; it is very easy to find at this stage.

The Lulworth Skipper prefers rough, unfertilised grasslands where there is abundant Tor Grass exceeding 10 cm in height, growing on south-facing slopes sheltered from the wind. It is absent from the few unimproved, closely grazed grasslands. On most of the steep, calcareous, coastal slopes grazing has been abandoned and there is now a luxuriant growth of Tor Grass. In one such field we found that numbers increased twentyfold within three years as Tor Grass spread after the cessation of grazing. The predominance of tall coarse swards of Tor Grass, especially since the 1950s when rabbits were killed by myxomatosis, has been responsible for the present abundance of this butterfly.

Distribution and Status

A survey was made of all likely areas in 1978 and we believe that the map is virtually complete. This butterfly now occurs continuously along both the southern scarp of the chalk and the coastal limestones of Purbeck and westward along the coast to Osmington. West of Weymouth there are two small colonies at Burton Bradstock. Surprisingly, no colony has been recorded on the oolites, cornbrash and Portland limestone. The two old records in the centre of the County, that we have mapped, are authentic, but almost certainly originate from deliberate or accidental releases by early entomologists. Today neither Tor Grass nor Lulworth Skippers are present in these places. Eighty-three colonies of Lulworth Skipper were found in 1978 of which only 37 had previous records. Several consisted of tens and even hundreds of thousands of individuals. There is no doubt that today the Lulworth Skipper occurs in many more colonies, and is far more numerous than at any time since its discovery in 1832.

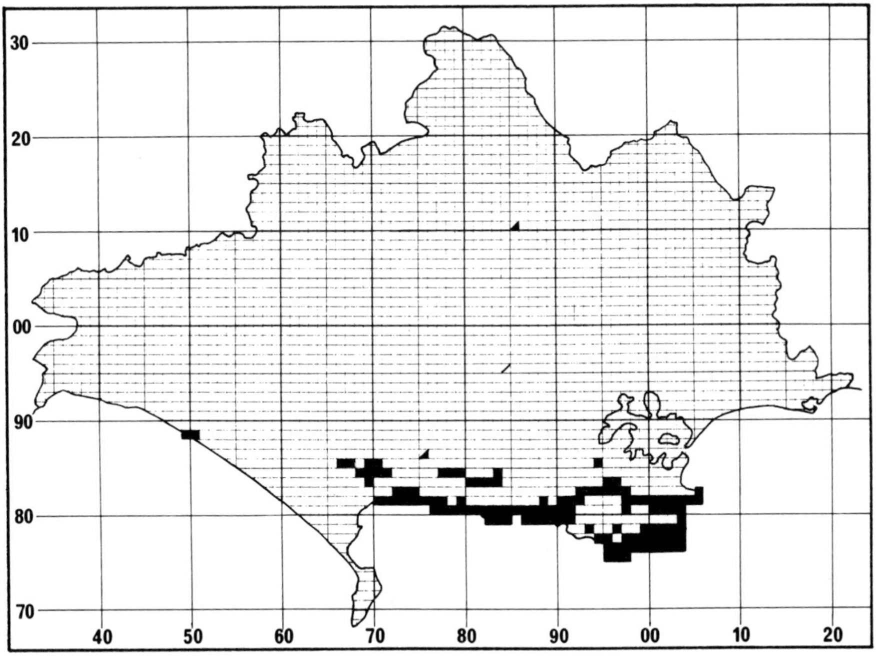

Where to see: Vast colonies occur on the calcareous grasslands in the vicinity of the Lulworth Range, on undercliffs at Osmington and Ringstead Bay, and in tall grassland on the coast of Purbeck.

When to see: Adults, July and August. Larvae, search for notched Tor Grass or stripped midribs containing a short double length of blade, fastened by silk, in early June.

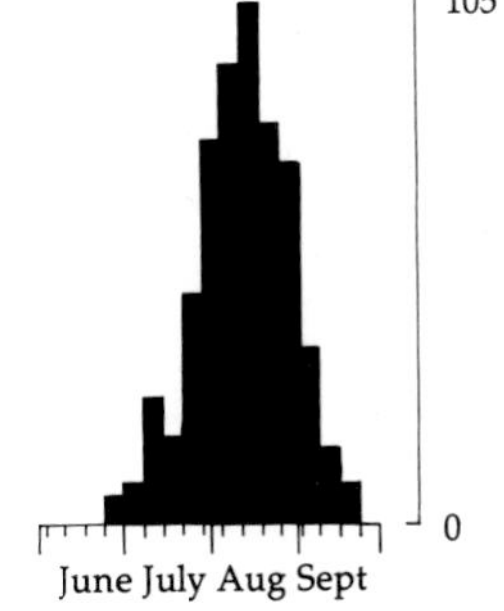

SILVER-SPOTTED SKIPPER – *Hesperia comma* Plate 5

This beautiful, but rare, Skipper is really an insect of central and southern Europe which maintains a toe-hold on the chalk downs of southern England. The larvae feed on Sheep's Fescue (*Festuca ovina*), which is still common in most of the fragments of calcareous grassland which have escaped agricultural improvement. The butterfly is much rarer than its foodplant. Even so, its past and present rarity on the warm downlands of Dorset is puzzling; many more colonies have been recorded from Hampshire, Surrey and as far north as the Chilterns.

The Silver-spotted Skipper occurs in self-contained colonies that have generally bred on the same discrete sites for centuries. Less than a hectare of suitable open downland can support a colony, but most sites are slightly larger and occur on steep, sheltered, thin-soiled, south-facing slopes, especially where the turf is sparse and grows among crumbly chalk scree and where the sun bakes the ground. The females are fussy over egg-laying, placing their eggs singly on small fescue plants that abut onto the bare ground. Plants growing in a dense sward are invariably rejected but young plants, in sunny depressions, are especially chosen. The large, curiously attractive, pudding-basin shaped eggs can be found easily from late summer until the spring once one is able to recognise suitable fescue plants. The eggs hatch in the spring, when each larva forms a silken nest from which it emerges to feed at night. The caterpillar is the ugliest of all our butterflies', resembling a fat, greenish-grey maggot.

In the past, suitable swards were created by fairly heavy grazing, but today the Silver-spotted Skipper (with the Adonis Blue and chalk colonies of Grayling and Silver-studded Blue) has become a casualty of the decline in intensive grazing on unfertilised downs, the loss of rabbits and agricultural improvement.

Distribution and Status

Dale described the Silver-spotted Skipper as 'rare' in Dorset, but for Bankes and Parkinson Curtis it was 'common very locally' in the 19th and early 20th centuries. The map shows that it was once widely distributed on the central and northern chalk scarp from Cheselbourne north-eastwards to the County border. Other well-known colonies bred on earthworks and on flatter ground, such as at Badbury Rings and near Blandford. Curiously, there are no reliable records for Purbeck. Most colonies disappeared in the first half of this century, yet in the early 1970s the butterfly was still present in 17 1 km squares, representing about eight colonies. Since then these have decreased to probably two sites, both nature reserves, in the County and to only 54 in Britain. There is a small colony, straddling the County boundary, on Martin Down, although most individuals breed on the Hampshire side. The finest colony, of several thousand butterflies, is on Fontmell Down which in 1981 was the among the seven largest in Britain. Despite detailed surveys in 1978 and 1981, it is possible, but unlikely, that other colonies may survive, since this butterfly is easily overlooked. This species has declined throughout Britain, and everywhere depends on the correct management of the remaining sites.

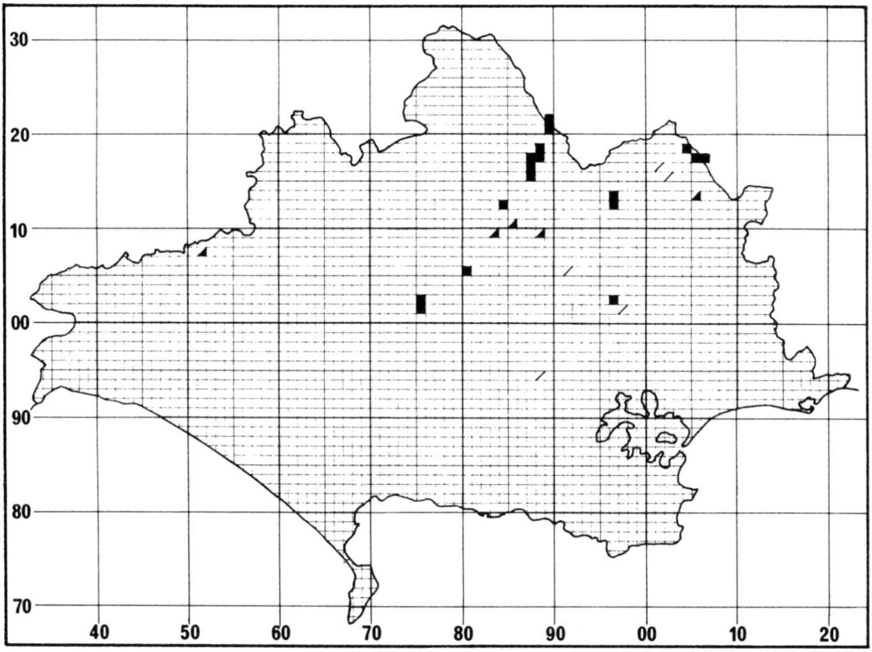

Where to see: From the footpaths on Fontmell Down. Collecting is prohibited as this is a National Trust property, part of which is managed as a nature reserve by the Dorset Naturalists' Trust.

When to see: Adults from late July until August. It is the latest Skipper to emerge, just overlapping with the similar Large Skipper. Eggs are easily found on small plants of Sheep's Fescue in sparse turf in the autumn.

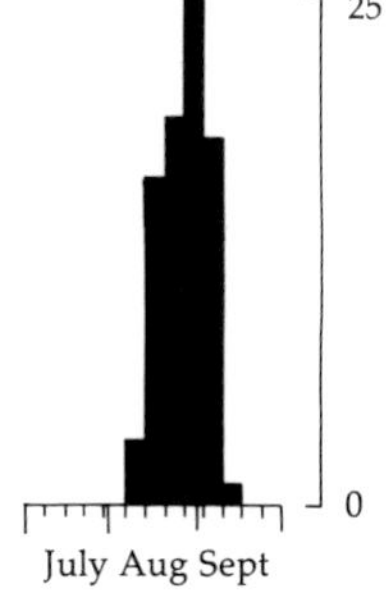

LARGE SKIPPER – *Ochlodes venata* Plate 6

This is one of two Skippers that are to be found commonly throughout Dorset in the summer. The Large Skipper is perhaps more abundant and widespread than the Small Skipper, and, as with that species, the map gives a poor impression of its distribution in the County.

The adults have one generation a year and fly about two weeks earlier than the Small Skipper, although there is a considerable overlap in their flight periods. The wings of the Large Skipper have distinctive mottled orange and brown markings that are more pronounced in the females than in the males. It is unlikely to be confused with any other species except the Silver-spotted Skipper, which is very rare in Dorset and flies about one month later.

Female Large Skippers lay their eggs underneath the leaves of Cocksfoot (*Dactylis glomerata*), and occasionally other grasses. The young larva hides within a tube made from the folded leaf blade. It hibernates in a sturdier tube and resumes feeding in the spring. Cocksfoot is a very common and widely distributed grass in Dorset occurring in woods, hedgerows, grassland and on disturbed ground on all soil types in the County with the exception of heathland. The distribution of the Large Skipper is similar to that of its food plant, occurring almost everywhere where the grass is allowed to grow fairly tall. The butterfly occurs in more or less discrete colonies which can survive at very low numbers on small areas or strips of land, such as road verges and hedgebanks. Although common in overgrown open grassland, the Large Skipper is characteristic of sunny patches of tall grass that are sheltered by shrubs and trees. The adult is a familiar sight feeding on bramble along wood edges, in glades, and along rides. Huge populations sometimes develop in young plantations in the years before the grasses decline because of shading from the growing trees. Ironically, this grassland butterfly nowadays is more likely to be seen in the neighbourhood of woods than in fields in the flatter parts of the County, where intensive farming has eliminated Cocksfoot from the sward.

Distribution and Status

The Large Skipper is much more widely distributed than the map suggests, for it is often overlooked or ignored. Its distribution in the west of the County, where we believe it to be ubiquitous where native grasses survive, is particularly poorly represented. Its lowest numbers are confined to local pockets in a broad belt of intensively cultivated land stretching from west of Dorchester to Blandford and Wimborne, and in the unwooded parts of the Blackmoor Vale. It is also rather local on the heathlands of the south-east where it is confined to enriched grassy areas, especially where these are sheltered by gorse scrub. The Large Skipper is virtually absent from the conurbations of Poole and Bournemouth. Otherwise it is a common insect wherever wild grasses grow freely.

In the past, the Large Skipper was undoubtedly much commoner than today. Date listed it as being 'generally distributed' and Parkinson Curtis wrote of the first half of this century: 'the most widely spread and generally common of the family . . . a list of localities would serve no purpose.'

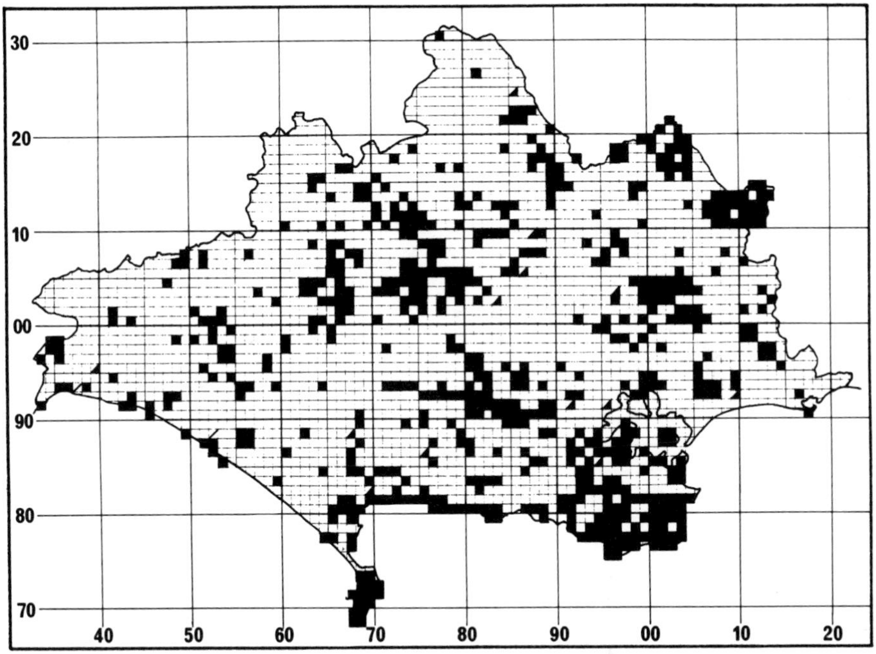

Where to see: Any warm sunny, sheltered place where there is a tall growth of wild grasses; especially in woods and scrubby areas.

When to see: There is one adult generation a year, beginning in early June and reaching a peak at the end of the month. A few worn individuals survive into August and occasionally even until September.

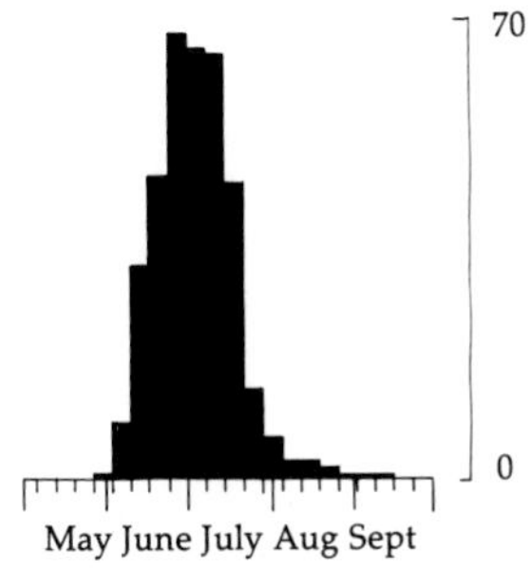

DINGY SKIPPER – *Erynnis tages* Plate 7

This drab, rather moth-like butterfly is often overlooked, but with practice it is not difficult to spot, and, on close examination, proves to be unexpectedly attractive. The adults emerge in the spring, and on sunny days alternate between basking with their wings widely spread and making rapid darting flights from flower to flower. In dull weather they often rest with the wings draped round a dead flower head, again enhancing their moth-like appearance.

Dingy Skippers occur in discrete colonies and are seldom seen far from their breeding sites. Colonies are often small, consisting of less than 100 adults, although a few of several hundred individuals are known in Dorset. They are found where the usual larval foodplant, Bird's-foot Trefoil (*Lotus corniculatus*) grows in abundance, preferably in large clumps on sunny slopes or in warm depressions, especially if these are scattered over an acre or more. Smaller warm banks with Bird's-foot Trefoil, such as railway cuttings, also often have colonies, but the butterfly rarely occurs on road verges and other similar exposed strips of grassland.

Typical sites for the Dingy Skipper occur all along the coastline where there are undercliffs, dunes or rough broken land. There are colonies on most of the unimproved chalk and limestone grasslands in the County, especially on their south facing slopes, and on unfertilised downs with a poor flora, but with abundant Bird's-foot Trefoil. On richer downs, Horseshoe Vetch (*Hippocrepis comosa*) is an alternative foodplant. In both cases, downs that are lightly grazed have the largest colonies. Heavy uniform grazing is unsuitable, and if grazing is abandoned the foodplants quickly decline.

Much smaller colonies also occur in many woods, where Bird's-foot Trefoil grows in sunny, sheltered clearings. On heavy soils, such as the northern clays, Bird's-foot Trefoil is usually restricted to the tops of anthills, but here the Dingy Skipper also makes use of the Greater Bird's-foot Trefoil (*Lotus uliginosus*) as foodplant.

Distribution and Status

Until the last war, the Dingy Skipper was 'generally' or 'well distributed throughout Dorset', 'common to very common in suitable localities'. This is no longer the case. It is now distinctly local, although undoubtedly more widespread than the map suggests, since the species is often overlooked. There has been no apparent decline along the coast, where there are many more colonies to be recorded and where one still expects to see this butterfly almost anywhere in springtime. Further inland, it is now much more local because agricultural improvements have destroyed much suitable chalk downland; it survives as scattered relicts, chiefly on steep slopes. In woods there has been a similar decline due to the decrease in coppicing, but where this still occurs, colonies may be expected. Very small colonies breed along the broad mown rides of some conifer plantations, and in the Blackmoor Vale the Dingy Skipper survives in most woodland clearings. It has never been a common butterfly on heathland and is absent from heather areas. However it breeds along a few banks and tracks where chalk rubble has been laid.

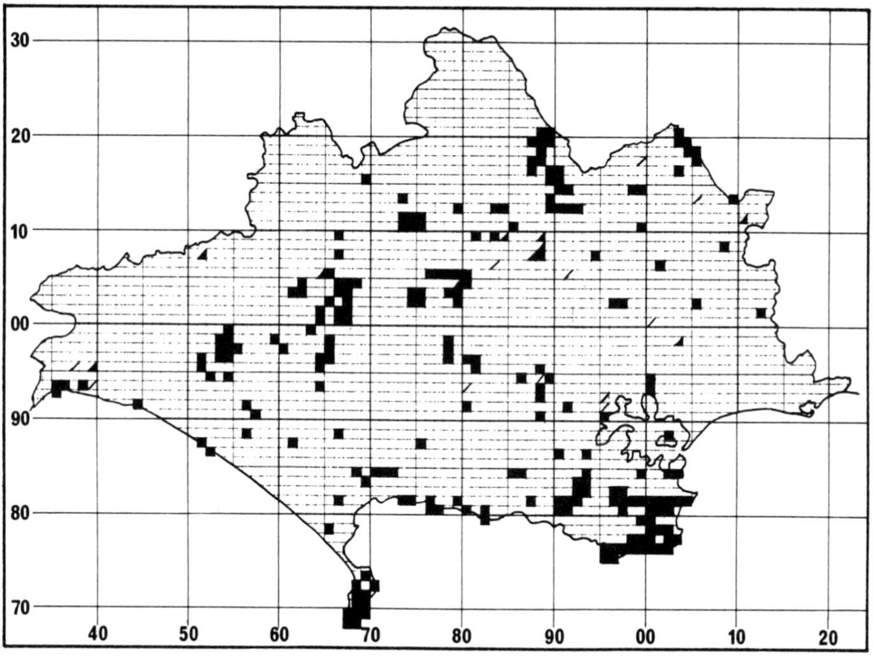

Where to see: Rough, coastal, undercliff grasslands; any south-facing unimproved downland.

When to see: Adults in late May and June, occasional second brood adults in August, as shown opposite. Look for the bright-orange eggs at the bases of the leaflets of the foodplants from June until early July.

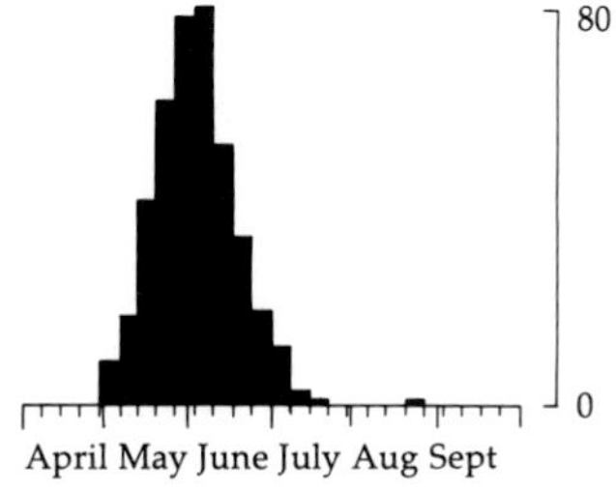

GRIZZLED SKIPPER – *Pyrgus malvae* Plate 8

This is the earliest of the six Dorset skippers to emerge, and is sometimes seen in late April in a warm year. However, the main flight period is mid-May to mid-June, overlapping considerably with that of its close relative, the Dingy Skipper. There are still several places in the County where the two species fly together. In such cases, the Dingy Skipper predominates in the more open areas, while the Grizzled Skipper prefers sheltered nooks. This butterfly is one of the smallest species, and has distinctive black and white chequered markings on the wings. It is unlikely to be confused with any other butterfly, although it can be mistaken for a dayflying moth, of which there are several rather similar species.

The Grizzled Skipper is found in discrete colonies which are often restricted to very small areas of land. Most populations are small and usually contain fewer than 100 individuals. The main larval foodplant in Dorset is Wild Strawberry (*Fragaria vesca*), although Tormentil (*Potentilla erecta*), Silverweed (*P. anserina*), and even Blackberry and Raspberry may be used. The eggs are laid underneath the leaves. The young larvae feed on the leaves protected at first by silk pads and, eventually, by a coccoon of silk and leaves. The insect hibernates as a pupa, remaining in this stage for about nine months.

Most Grizzled Skipper colonies are to be found where the food plant grows in sunny, sheltered situations, often among quite sparse, but not necessarily very short vegetation. Typical sites are warm, crumbling banks; rough, sheltered grassland among scrub on the downs; and clearings at the edges of woods. Young coppice is also ideal, especially on the chalk where Wild Strawberry is common in the ground flora. Some small colonies occur along the broadest, mown, grassy rides of conifer plantations.

Distribution and Status

Dale described the Grizzled Skipper as being 'generally distributed' during the 19th century, but Parkinson Curtis thought this assessment needed qualification for the present century. Around 1960, he wrote 'it is not by any means everywhere and there are large areas of heathland where the insect is absent'. Since then there have been many more losses because of the improvement of calcareous grasslands for agriculture, the decline in the amount of coppiced woodland and the general tidying up of the countryside. It is not yet a rare butterfly in the County, but has become localised and is considerably scarcer than the Dingy Skipper. Today, its strongholds are the steep slopes of the chalk scarp from Eggardon to Shaftesbury, and its distribution in this area is probably not adequately represented by the map. To the north-west there are a few small colonies in woods in the Blackmoor Vale. In contrast to the Dingy Skipper, this species is a much rarer butterfly in south-east Dorset. There are a few colonies in the Purbeck Hills but some of the squares on the map from this area represent strays. It is virtually absent from the coast, with the exception of a few areas of rough limestone grassland in Purbeck. Despite the abundance of Tormentil, colonies have always been rare on the heathlands and have only occurred in a few areas where the soil is richer.

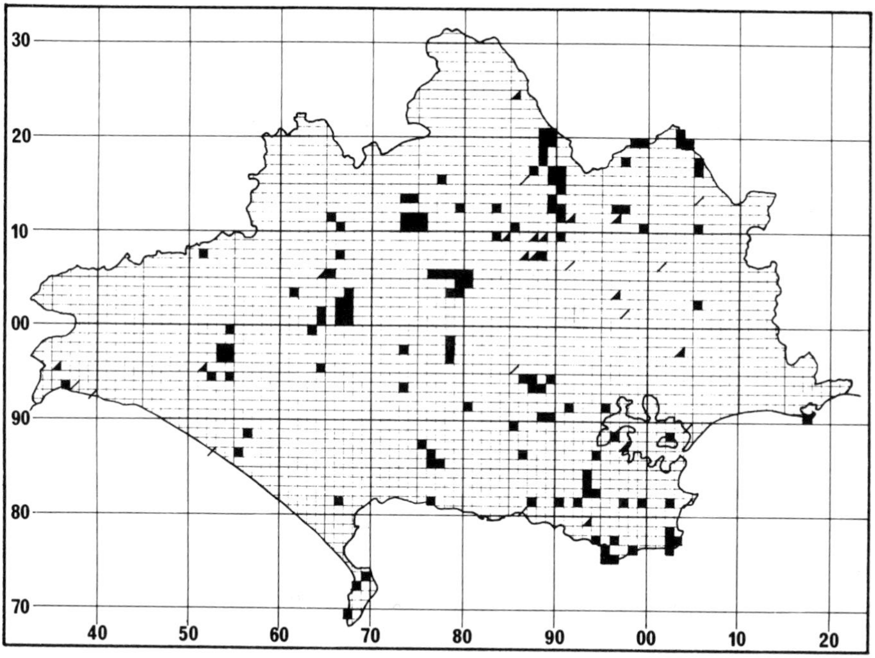

Where to see: Natural grassland adjoining woodland or scrubby areas on the northern chalk. There is a large colony on Fontmell Down.

When to see: Adults in late April in a warm year, otherwise in May and June. Occasional second brood adults emerge in July.

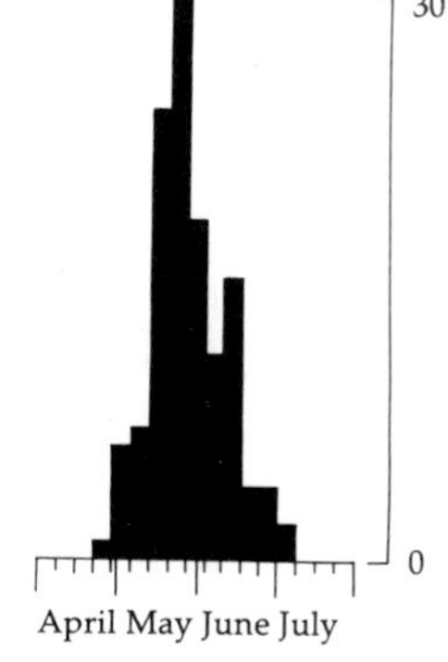

WOOD WHITE – *Leptidea sinapis* Plate 17

This woodland butterfly is one of the rarest species in the County, we know of only two populations. It was considerably more common until late Victorian times but the habitats changed and the colonies became extinct. The Wood White is a fairly sedentary species and natural recolonisation seldom takes place from the remaining colonies. Because of this, in the last 30 years man-made introductions have been common and at least one Dorset colony owes its origin to this practice.

This is an attractive, small butterfly with a slow and fluttering flight. The males seem to be in perpetual motion as they hover or slowly patrol woodland rides searching for mates. Although the Wood White is distinctive in both appearance and in flight, small, weakly-flying examples of the Green-veined White may be mistaken for it, unless they are carefully examined. Wood Whites emerge in late May and early June and there is often a small second brood in August. The eggs are laid on leguminuous plants including Meadow Vetchling (*Lathryus pratensis*), Bitter Vetch (*L. montanus*), Tufted Vetch (*Vicia cracca*) and Bird's-foot Trefoil (*Lotus corniculatus*). Plants which are sheltered yet unshaded or only lightly shaded are preferred. The caterpillar feeds on the leaves of these plants.

The heyday of the Wood White was the early 19th century and earlier, when nearly all woods were coppiced. Most, if not all, Dorset colonies became extinct when coppicing ceased. Suitable conditions for this butterfly are sometimes created in modern conifer plantations but these gradually become too shady unless the rides are very broad. We know of no example of a modern plantation in Dorset which has a colony. Railway embankments, where vetches are allowed to grow luxuriantly among developing scrub, also provide suitable habitats. One of the Dorset colonies is an introduction on such a site 10 years ago: nine butterflies were released and a further six in 1976 which were taken from a colony near the Somerset border. The introduced colony is now very large. The other colony in the County is believed to be original. It is established in an area of rough grassland surrounded by ancient woodland.

Distribution and Status

Dale, referring to the first half of the 19th century, wrote 'scarce in Purbeck, does not occur in Portland but is frequently taken in wooded districts of the County.' Bankes, too, was frustratingly terse: 'not uncommon in well-wooded districts'. Few of the old records give detailed localities and so the map is a poor representation of the past distribution. Commenting on these statements (probably in the 1950s), Parkinson Curtis wrote, 'whatever may have been the case prior to 1895, these estimates do not pertain today. I have never yet seen nor taken this insect in Dorset'. However, he refers to a few reports of occasional specimens in the west.

We believe the Wood White to be confined to two, possibly three localities in Dorset. Of the two near the Somerset border, one exists today and the other which provided specimens for the third colony, survived until 1976 but is now believed to be extinct. The recent record from the south-west coast is probably a stray from colonies breeding on the undercliff just over the border in Devon. Other single adults have been reported from elsewhere in Dorset but are believed to be strays, releases or misidentified Green-veined Whites. They are not included on the map.

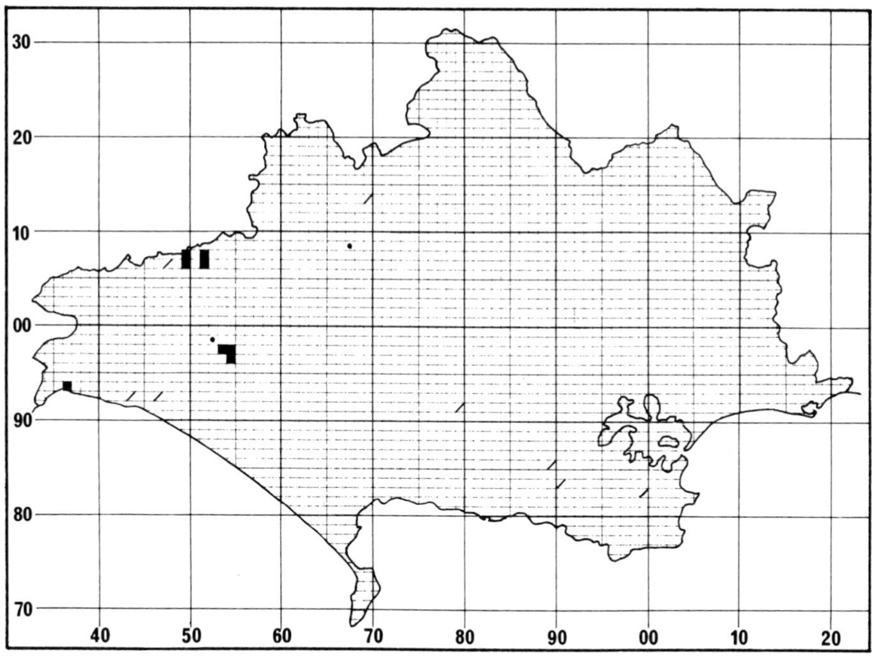

Where to see: Neither Dorset locality has public access. The nearest accessible colony is on the undercliffs west of Lyme Regis.

When to see: Late May, building to a peak in early June, with a small second brood in August.

CLOUDED YELLOW – *Colias croceus* Plate 9

This is one of the two yellow butterflies to be regularly seen in Dorset. In most years it is much rarer than the Brimstone, from which it may be distinguished by its more sulphurous colour, black wingtips and conventional shape. There is also a pale greyish form of the female named *helice* which may form up to a quarter of the females, although usually the proportion is much lower. These distinctive females are often misidentified as the rarer Berger's Clouded Yellow or as the Pale Clouded Yellow.

The Clouded Yellow is a migratory butterfly and occurs in greatly differing numbers each year. It is unable to survive even the mildest British winters, except in insignificant numbers. Parkinson Curtis offers good evidence for overwintering at Swanage, Parkstone and Burton Bradstock but the vast majority of Clouded Yellows seen in the County are immigrants from southern Europe reaching the south coast of Britain in late May or early June in most, if not every year. Their numbers are usually small and they are rarely seen. Immigration to Dorset from far out to sea has been watched by Parkinson Curtis (using binoculars) on at least three occasions, by Dannreuther at Worth Matravers in 1936, and by Frohawk. The adults have a strong purposeful flight and are not diverted along the coast once the shoreline has been reached but proceed onto the Downs and throughout the County. The Clouded Yellow does not form discrete colonies but may be seen as single individuals almost anywhere including gardens and towns. There are, however, favoured habitats, notably the flowery chalk downs. For example in 1983, numbers on Ballard Down were more than 30 times greater than on the heathland at Studland 3 km away.

The females lay their eggs on leguminous plants, mainly clovers, although Alfalfa is also a favourite. It is interesting that this is the only species of butterfly that is able to breed freely in modern farmland in which clovers are often important sown constituents. The caterpillars eat the leaves and after pupation, the adults emerge about seven to eight weeks after the previous generation. This homebred generation is much larger than the immigrant one and if immigrant adults are noticed in June, it is a good sign that large numbers will be seen in August. There may be a smaller third generation in the autumn.

Distribution and Status

Numbers vary greatly each year, depending on the arrival of immigrants. Occasionally, large flights arrive in June to produce 'Clouded Yellow Years' when the butterfly is common throughout the County. These years occurred fairly regularly in the past, but in the intervening years the butterfly was scarce or even absent. Notable Clouded Yellow Years in this century were 1947 and 1949. The former year was 'unparalleled', when 'incredible' numbers occurred as 'swarms'. After 1949 numbers were consistently lower. It was not unusual to see one or two adults on the coastal downs in August, but no more, and it was widely believed that Clouded Yellow Years were a thing of the past because of modernisation of agriculture on the Continent. Then, in 1983, there was an immigration to match any previously except that of 1947. Records were received from all over Dorset and the map for 1983 alone is reproduced. This represents little more than the chance distribution of recorders in August 1983. On the flowery downs it was possible to see 20 or 30 adults at once, and white *helice* females were common. Alas, numbers were back to normal in 1984.

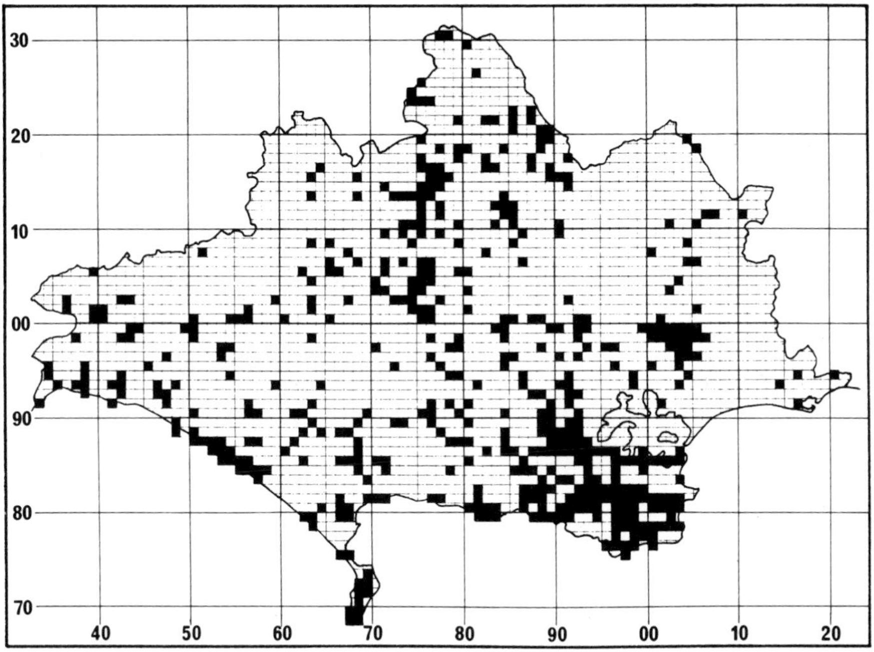

Where to see: Anywhere, but especially on the flowery downs near the coast.

When to see: The main flight is in early August. The third generation is only just evident on the histograms and extends well into October, beyond our recording season.

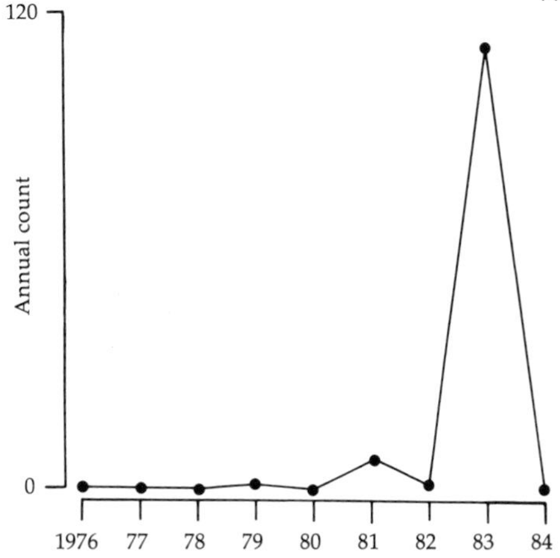

Clouded Yellow on the Swanage transect.

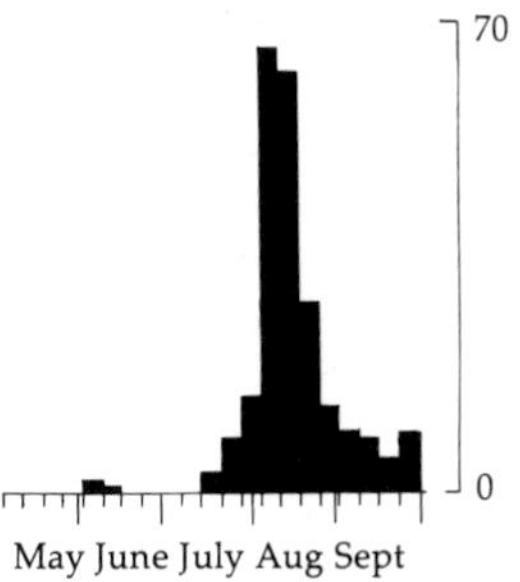

BRIMSTONE – *Gonepteryx rhamni* Plate 10

Any large yellow butterfly seen on warm days in the spring or late summer is almost certainly a male Brimstone. The pale female is less often noticed, or is dismissed as Large White. The Brimstone is a mobile species that does not live in fixed colonies, but flies widely in search of the larval foodplant. The eggs are laid on either Purging Buckthorn (*Rhamnus cathartica*) or Alder Buckthorn (*Frangula alnus*) and the caterpillars eat the leaves. These shrubs grow, respectively, mainly on dry chalk soils or most acid soils. The eggs are laid in late spring on sheltered, sunny bushes growing in scrub, hedgerows, and woodland edges, glades and rides. Adults emerge over a long period in midsummer and gorge themselves on nectar before hibernating. They reappear on the first warm days in the following spring. Although common, the adult is generally seen in ones and twos in most of Dorset, except in wooded districts where the foodplants are abundant. There they may gather in large numbers to feed on Teasels and Thistles in the late summer. They also often visit gardens at this time.

Distribution and Status

As one of the wandering species of butterfly in Dorset, it would undoubtedly be possible, with persistent searching, to find a Brimstone in every 1 km square. The map is clearly incomplete, but gives a reasonable picture of the local abundance of this butterfly and hence one's chance of seeing it. The map mirrors the distributions of the two Buckthorns recorded by Good in his *Botanical Survey of Dorset,* and should be compared with other mobile butterflies, such as Peacock, Small Tortoiseshell, and Large and Small White which, we believe more closely reflect the effort of recorders.

Of Purging Buckthorn, Good writes that it is common and widely but incompletely distributed in hedges and thickets on calcareous soils. Plentiful on the central and northern chalk, and locally frequent in the northern vales west of the River Stour. Much less frequent elsewhere, especially in the south of the County'. So it is with the Brimstone: there are numerous records from the wooded areas of the Blackmoor Vale and the central and northern chalk, but many fewer from the flatter, intensively farmed areas, such as south of Blandford and around Dorchester. Most interesting is the dearth of records from the well recorded Purbeck Hills and the coastal limestones, including Portland, where most other mobile species are well represented.

Of Alder Buckthorn, Good writes 'Frequent but rather local in acid bogs, chiefly in the Poole Basin, especially in the peaty valleys around Wareham, but also in parts of the northern vales and on the western Greensands'. The Brimstone, one notes, is almost ubiquitous on the acid soils of Purbeck and round the Poole Basin to the Hampshire border. There are scattered records throughout the west of the County. There is no evidence to indicate that the Brimstone has declined in Dorset since the 19th century, when Dale described it without qualification as 'common'. One can infer that frequent, but not serious, local declines have occurred through the loss of the foodplants in woodland clearances, modern silviculture, the destruction of hedgerows, and the intensification of farming on the flatter chalk areas. On the other hand, Purging Buckthorn has increased on some downs that were formerly grassland when grazed by sheep and rabbits.

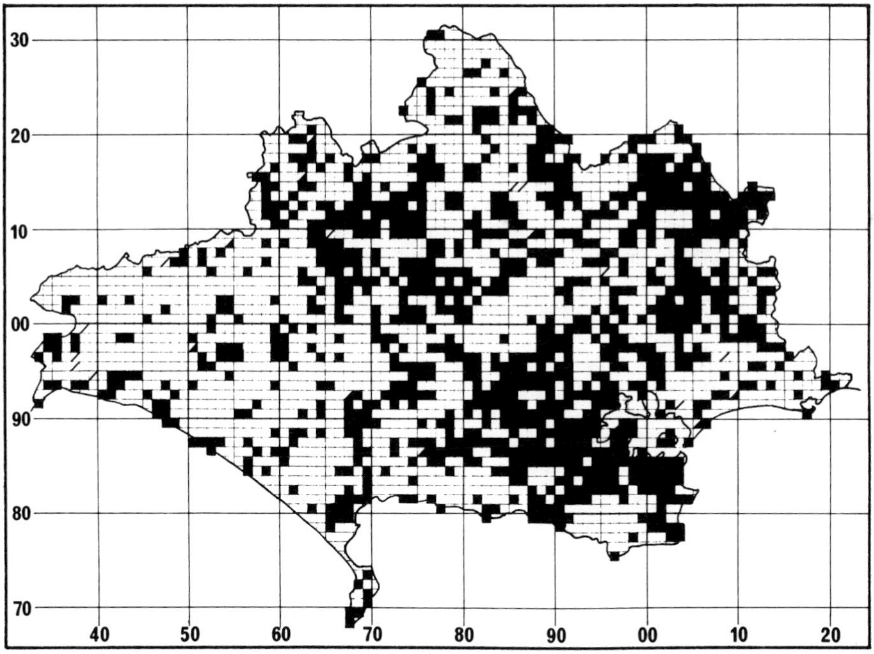

Where to see: Especially in wooded areas on the northern chalk between Milton Abbas and Shaftesbury; among wet scrub besides the heathlands around Wareham.

When to see: The single generation of adults may be seen in any month from March to October, but mainly after emergence in August and after hibernation in April.

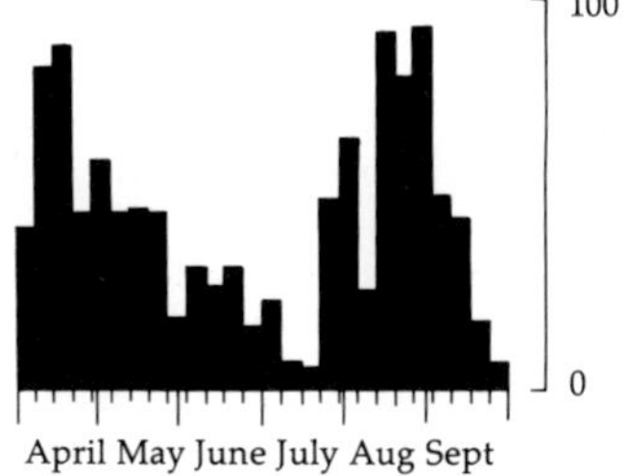

LARGE WHITE – *Pieris brassicae* Plate 15

As its name implies, this is the largest white butterfly to be seen in Dorset. It is also one of the commonest and, were it not for its reputation as a pest of cabbage plants, it would probably also be considered one of our most beautiful species.

The eggs are laid in yellow clusters of fifty or more beneath the leaves of Cabbages (*Brassica* spp.) in gardens, allotments and fields throughout the County. Occasionally, wild species of this family of plants may be used, including the Wild Cabbage (*Brassica oleracea*) which grows on the coast. The caterpillars are gregarious and defoliate the plants, feeding voraciously as they grow. The pupa is often found on sheds, fences and under windowsills.

The Large White is a highly mobile butterfly that does not form identifiable colonies. Adults may be seen flying anywhere in town, village and in the countryside, although they tend to congregate around cabbage crops. There are two broods a year, in late spring from hibernating pupae, and in late summer. The second brood is larger, but numbers in all years may be supplemented by immigrants from adjacent counties as well as from the continent. Parkinson Curtis noted a 'massive' immigration over Portland Bill in August 1964. He also quotes reports of southerly migrations from Britain from the diaries of Dr. A. A. Lisney: 'On 16th August 1951 at Dorchester and Weymouth a large migration of *P. brassicae* and *P. rapae* in the proportion of about 10 *brassicae* to one *rapae* observed going south. The migrating insects were sufficiently numerous to attract the attention of persons not generally interested in Natural History. On 17th August 1951 specimens were seen leaving Weymouth beach and flying out to sea. This movement continued steadily for 4 days and at the same intensity and then gradually tailed off. The exodus did not prevent the two species persisting more commonly than other butterflies in a year noteworthy for the general scarcity of Lepidoptera'. It is interesting that the spectacular inward and outward migrations noted by Parkinson Curtis were both in August. It is not known how important these movements are on the overall numbers of Large Whites in Dorset, but it is probable that most individuals are resident or come from neighbouring counties.

Distribution and Status

Adults occur thoughout Dorset in all habitats, although they are much commoner in localities where cabbages grow. The map reflects the main areas for recorders and would be entirely black if recording had covered the whole County. Numbers fluctuate greatly from year to year, possibly due to immigration, but are rarely abundant enough to cause serious damage to crops. Parkinson Curtis describes seeing the Large White 'in clouds' in 1940, although he 'never saw a specimen' in Dorset for a period of ten years in the early part of this century. Such extremes of abundance have not been repeated in the past 15 years, when the Large White has been common but rarely abundant. It is also described as 'common' in the 19th century by Dale and there is little reason to believe that its status has changed significantly in Dorset since his father began his *Entomological Journal* in 1808.

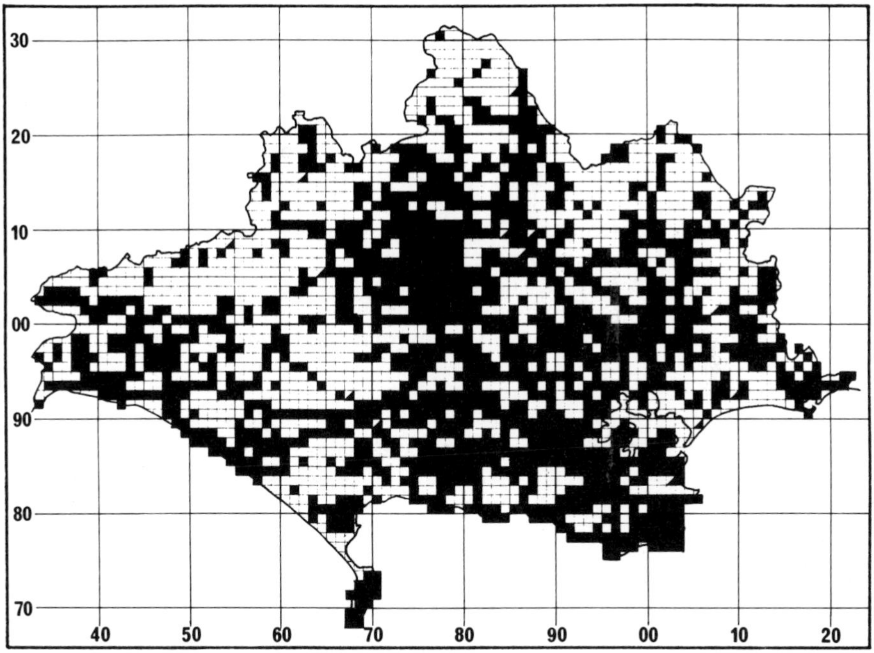

Where to see: Anywhere in the County, especially in vegetable gardens, allotments, and cabbage fields.

When to see: The first adults emerge in late April or early May, peaking in late May or June. The second generation peaks in August and may last into October. Search for larvae in July.

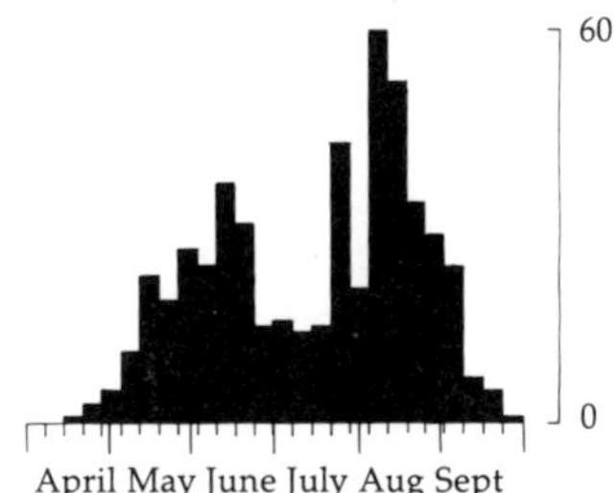

SMALL WHITE – *Pieris rapae* Plate 11

This is one of the commonest butterflies in the County. It is a highly mobile species that wanders through the countryside in search of wild species of Crucifer, garden nasturtiums, and, especially, cultivated Brassicas, on which to lay its eggs. It is the smaller of the two Cabbage Whites and, has a penchant for laying its eggs on slightly sheltered Brassicas, such as those plants growing near hedgerows or in gardens.

This is a very mobile butterfly and the native populations are regularly reinforced by immigrants from the Continent. A return flight has also been reported, similar to that described for the Large White. These migrations make little apparent impact on numbers in most years, and we believe that most Small Whites seen in Dorset are home bred or are from neighbouring counties.

Distribution and Status

The Small White is ubiquitous in the County in most years. The map, if complete, would be entirely black. We consider this species to be equally numerous on all soils and in all regions, with local concentrations around gardens, allotments and cabbage fields. Numbers fluctuate greatly and sometimes may be swollen by migrants. Fluctuations recorded from 1976 to 1984 on the Swanage butterfly transect show that the summer brood was consistently larger than the spring brood. However, it is impossible to predict from the size of the first brood whether numbers will rise to pest proportions in the second. This occurred in 1977, but negligible numbers emerged in the summer of 1980, after a spring brood that had been larger than that in 1977. It is interesting to note that the three largest second broods of this period occured during the three coolest summers – 1977, 1978 and 1979 – and that these emergences greatly exceed the populations of 1976, 1982, 1983 and 1984, when the summers were exceptionally warm and dry. We do not know whether this is a reliable gauge for predicting outbreaks, or merely coincidence.

Parkinson Curtis wrote that, in the first half of this century, numbers of the Small White had also fluctuated greatly but had rarely risen to the position of a pest. Unlike the Large White, he never knew it to be 'devastatingly abundant'. In 1976-84, the Small White was consistently more numerous than the Large White, but was not devastating. Dale simply described this butterfly as 'common' and we have no reason to believe that it has changed in status since the early 19th century.

Where to see: Anywhere in town or country, often flying along hedges. In gardens and especially in cabbage patches, allotments and cabbage fields.

When to see: The two main broods are clearly shown in the histogram. There may, possibly, be a third or even a fourth emergence in some years, and adults can be seen well into October, after our recording period.

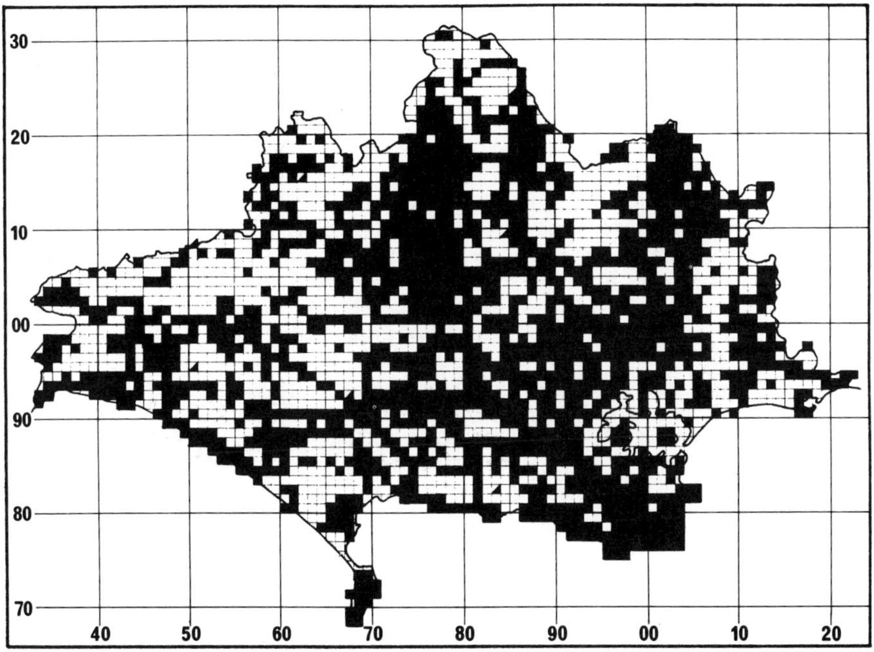

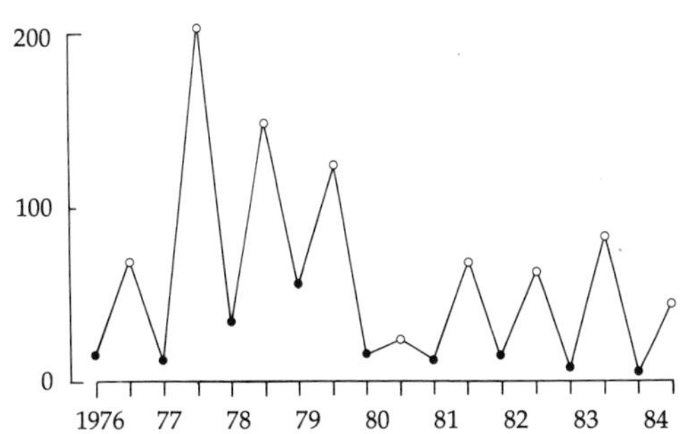

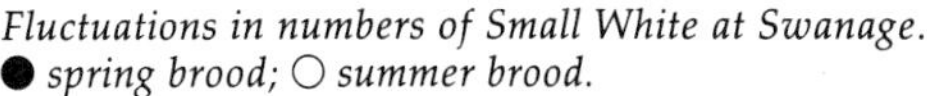

Fluctuations in numbers of Small White at Swanage.
● *spring brood;* ○ *summer brood.*

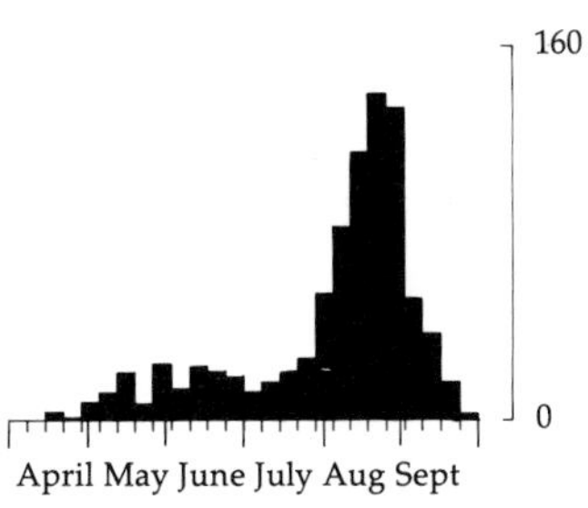

GREEN-VEINED WHITE – *Pieris napi* Plate 12

There are few commoner butterflies in Dorset than the Green-veined White, yet many naturalists are unfamiliar with it. Far too often it is dismissed without a second glance as a Small White, which is a pity, for it is a most attractive butterfly. There are two generations a year, in spring and in mid-summer. The wing markings differ between both broods and between the sexes. In both sexes the markings on the upper surfaces are bolder in the second generation, and the females are more heavily marked than the males, with black veins and spots. It is the distinctive underwing which gives the species its name. To quote Margaret Brooks, 'the hindwing is yellow, and the veins are outlined in black, giving an illusion of green'. In contrast to the markings on the upperwings, those on the underwings are sharpest in the first (spring) generation.

The eggs are laid on the undersides of the leaves of members of the Crucifer family and, as a rule, are quite easy to find. The commonest plants used are Watercress (*Nasturtium officinale*), Lady's Smock (*Cardamine pratensis*), Hedge Mustard (*Sisymbrium officinale*), Garlic Mustard (*Alliaria petiolata*) but probably many others are also eaten. These eggs are most often found on quite small plants growing in marshy spots. The caterpillar is similar to that of the Small White and rests on the leaves on which it feeds. Hibernation takes place during the pupal stage.

The Green-veined White has a weak fluttering flight. Nevertheless, it is a fairly mobile butterfly, although much less so than either the Large or Small Whites. It is believed to fly freely over large areas and not to form discrete colonies, as do many butterflies. Despite this, it occurs in the greatest densities on its preferred breeding areas. These are mainly damp places especially old meadows, woodland rides and along the banks of streams. In such areas the Green-veined White can often be very abundant, but in dry areas it is much less common.

Distribution and Status

The Green-veined White occurs throughout Dorset. The map is a poor representation of its status, especially in the west of the County. It is very common wherever Crucifers grow. The best areas are on damp or heavy soils, in unimproved meadows, along the sides of ditches, hedgerows and along woodland rides in the west of the County and on the northern clays. Although ubiquitous and locally abundant in such areas, it was probably much more numerous in the past, since many damp fields have been drained, eliminating its foodplants. It is also common in woods on the chalk, but is rarely seen on dry open downland or on the dry heathlands. It is also scarce in the open, intensively farmed, arable areas, such as the flatter chalklands from Dorchester to Wimborne. Nevertheless, it may be found locally in the small damp corners of rough ground which remain in this belt.

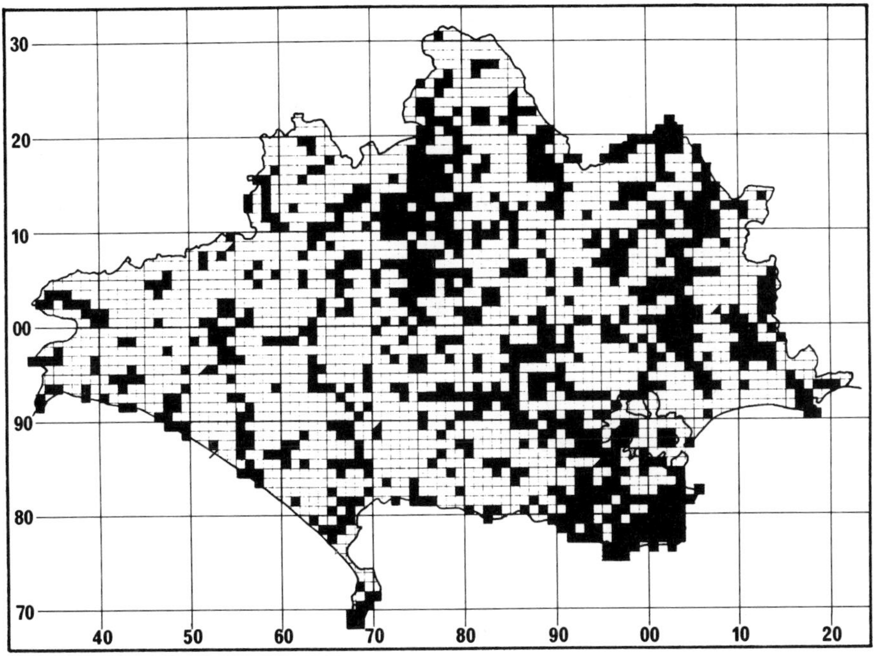

Where to see: Any damp rough grassland; woodland rides and clearings.

When to see: Adults in May and June and again in mid-summer; search for eggs in June and August.

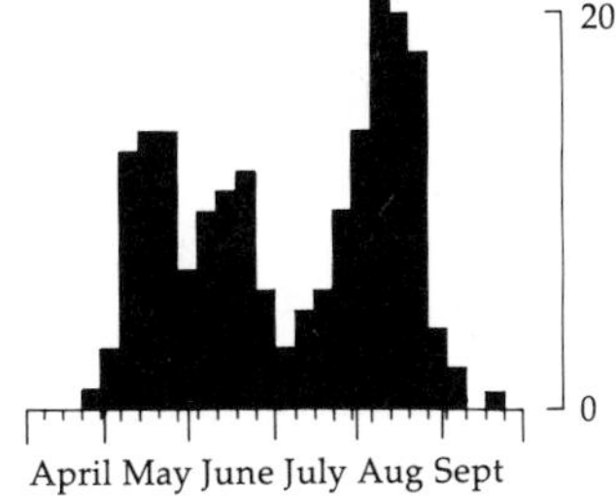

ORANGE TIP – *Anthocharis cardamines* Plates 13, 14 and 16

The Orange Tip is a comparatively mobile butterfly and the conspicuous males may be seen, usually alone, flying in any habitat throughout the County in the late spring. It often strays into gardens but seldom lingers. The female lacks the bright orange wingtips of the male and is therefore noticed less often. However, she is equally mobile and ubiquitous; we searched for eggs in most parts of Dorset in 1982-84 and found them laid almost everywhere that the food plants grow and often on well isolated plants.

The small bottle-shaped egg is found easily in June and early July; over half of the records on the map are of this stage. The egg is white when laid but turns bright orange after a day or two. It is laid on the flowers of the larger species of the cabbage family (Cruciferae). In Dorset, Garlic Mustard (*Alliaria petiolata*) and Lady's Smock (*Cardamine pratensis*) are by far the most important foodplants, although Hedge Mustard (*Sisymbrium officinale*), which is much less common in the County, is sometimes used. The caterpillars feed on the developing seed pods and, by lying along them they are beautifully camouflaged. However, they are easy to find if the pods are examined in June and July. Breeding occurs where these plants flower and adults are most numerous where the plants are abundant. Lady's Smock grows mainly in unimproved meadows, rough grassland and sunny woodland rides and glades on heavy or damp soils throughout the County but especially where there are ground water gley soils. It is particularly abundant in many woodland clearings and some ancient meadows in the Blackmoor Vale and in unimproved meadows in the river valleys. Because of agricultural changes, Lady's Smock is much less abundant than in the past, and Garlic Mustard is now the main foodplant of the Orange Tip over most of Dorset. This is a common but local plant of banks, hedgerows and woodland edges, especially in the western and northern vales. Many eggs and larvae are destroyed when roadsides are cut in June and July.

Distribution and Status

Dale in the 19th century and subsequent authors described the Orange Tip simply as 'common' in Dorset, although Parkinson Curtis noted that it rarely bred and was less often seen on high downs, heathlands, gardens, or in heavily grazed meadows. This seems to be an accurate summary of the present situation, except that it has also been greatly reduced in open farmland everywhere and is now confined more to woodlands and road verges. It is sometimes said that less intensive hedge and verge trimming has increased its survival along edges and verges but we doubt that this would compensate for the widespread loss of Lady's Smock in open fields. Nevertheless, the adult can be still seen throughout the County and it breeds at low densities in suitable habitats everywhere. The map is, thus, far from complete. At present, the Orange Tip appears to be commonest along hedges, lanes and woodland edges in west Dorset and in the wooded parts of the Blackmoor Vale.

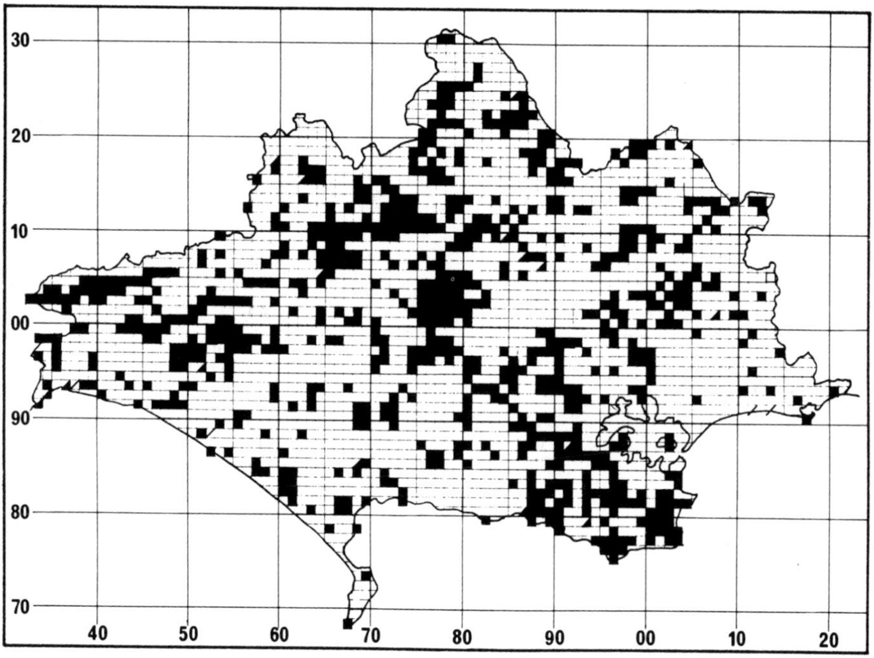

Where to see: Woodland edges, clearings and hedges everywhere, especially in the west and north. Rarer on dry soils, downs and heathlands.

When to see: Adults in April in a warm spring but mainly from mid May to mid June. Eggs and larvae may be found in June and July.

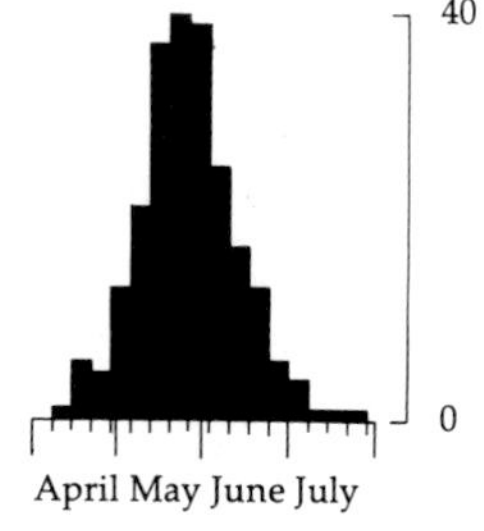

GREEN HAIRSTREAK – *Callophrys rubi* Plate 20

This is the second commonest of the four species of Hairstreak which breed in Dorset. It is the most frequently seen, because it is the only Hairstreak that lives among scrub and rough grassland and not the tree tops. Nevertheless it is hard to follow as it jinks rapidly between shrubs and it is even easier to miss at rest, when it perches on leaves with wings closed. Both Bankes and Parkinson Curtis consider that the undersides of Dorset specimens are more uniformly green, with fewer white spots, than elsewhere; specialists are referred to the latter's manuscript.

The Green Hairstreak breeds in small self-contained colonies of about 20-50 adults; in Dorset we have not encountered the huge populations that occasionally develop in other counties. The males spend most of their lives perched singly on the edges of prominent bushes, waiting for females to pass. Such perching posts may remain unchanged from year to year. The females fly freely over the hillsides, laying their eggs on suitable foodplants, mainly gorses (*Ulex* spp.) on the acid soils and Rockrose (*Helianthemum nummularium*) on calcareous soils. Eggs may also be laid on Bird's-foot Trefoil, Dyer's Greenweed, all vetches, and the flowers of Buckthorn and Dogwood. Most colonies occur in the gorsey parts of heathlands or on unimproved chalk and limestone downs. They may also be found in rough, unfertilised grasslands, undercliffs, the edges of woods, and clearings and young coppice. All sites are generally warm and sheltered with scattered shrubs, and are generally becoming scarcer in the County because of changes in land use, silviculture and agricultural practices.

Distribution and Status

The Green Hairstreak was considered by Dale to be 'generally distributed' in Dorset in the 19th century, which by today's standards, means that it was a common and widespread species. Early this century, Haines said it was 'very common in woods and bushy places throughout Dorset'. There has clearly been a considerable decline since those days, for the reasons already given. Thus, about 1960, Parkinson Curtis wrote, 'I should say very local although the colonies are numerous . . . each colony seems to keep within its own bounds until wiped out by improvements'. Twenty-five years later, 'numerous' is no longer an adjective that can be applied to this species in most of Dorset, least of all in the west, which Parkinson Curtis considered to be its stronghold. That region has been less well recorded than the others and the Green Hairstreak tends to be overlooked everywhere, nevertheless the absence of recent records from most of western Dorset is alarming. As usual for a fairly common species, old localities are missing from the map, because few entomologists bothered to list them. At present the Green Hairstreak is commonest, and is still to be expected, on any gorsey heath – hence the concentration of records in the Poole Basin. Its distribution and abundance on calcareous soils mirrors the status of the Rockrose: it is still locally common on unimproved downs on the northern chalk and in open wooded areas of Cranborne Chase, the Purbeck Hills and the chalk coast. A few scattered colonies occur elsewhere on the chalk, generally associated with woods, but the species is rare or absent on the limestones. Occasional colonies survive elsewhere on all soils, mainly in association with woodland.

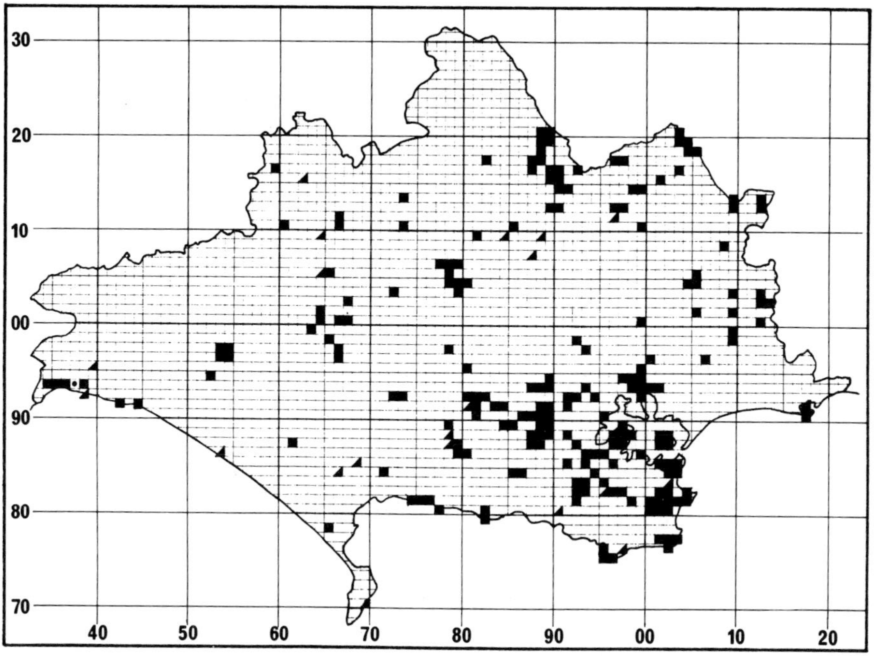

Where to see: Any gorsey heathland; chalk downs north of Swanage.

When to see: An extended single emergence, usually beginning in late May, reaching a peak a month later and continuing throughout July, sometimes even later.

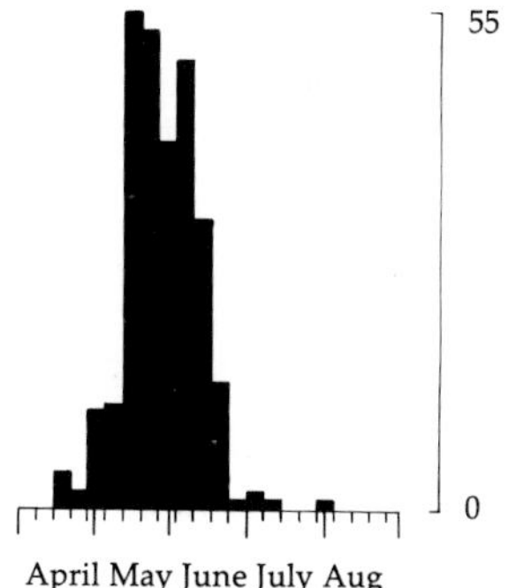

BROWN HAIRSTREAK – *Thecla betulae* Plate 21

This elusive butterfly is restricted to southern Britain and is one of the rarest species to occur in the County. It lives in permanent, self-contained colonies consisting of a small number of individuals. The eggs, larvae and pupae are distributed over a very wide area but the newly-emerged adults congregate at the top of a prominent tree or group of trees to mate. An Ash, usually growing at the edge of a wood is often chosen as the master tree. The adults rarely fly but remain perched on the tree tops, where they drink aphid honey dew. One is only likely to catch a brief glimpse of the female when she descends to lay eggs, usually singly, low down on Blackthorn (*Prunus spinosa*) or related shrubs. Egg laying takes place from mid-August until mid-September. The male Vapourer Moth, which is much more common in Dorset, may be mistaken for this butterfly, since it is of a similar size and colour and flies by day high among the tree tops.

The easiest way to locate the Brown Hairstreak is to search for its eggs during the winter on bare Blackthorn twigs. The eggs are laid on the young growth of prominent hedgerow plants or on small suckers. They are placed in a fork or at the base of a spine and, being white, are very conspicuous against the dark twigs. Each hatches at the end of April and the caterpillar feeds by night on the leaves of Blackthorn. It rests by day beautifully camouflaged on a silken pad beneath a leaf. It pupates on the ground in June.

The Brown Hairstreak occurs in districts on heavy soils where Blackthorn is common and where there are extensive woodlands interspersed with scrubby areas, copses and small hedged fields. This type of habitat is unusual in Dorset where most of the soils are well drained.

Distribution and Status

Old records exist for Purbeck, Bloxworth and Cranborne (none precise enough to have been mapped) but most sites, predictably, are on the clays of the Blackmoor Vale. Dale, who lived in this area, considered it to be a 'scarce and local' butterfly in the 19th century and Parkinson Curtis, Hayward and Bankes, spanning a century of entomology, failed to find it, although 'not due to any lack of assiduity'. In fact, it was almost certainly present when they searched, for this is an extremely easy species to miss unless one knows the trick of finding the eggs. One expert, T. W. Tolman, found them at Lydlinch recently, as have we, and we have also found large numbers around the wood edges and hedges near Kingston, one of Dale's old localities. The seven nearby squares on the map probably represent one large colony. Eggs were not found in 1984 at the other recently noted area, which no longer looks suitable. Nor have we found eggs at Dale's other localities, such as Middlemarsh. More surprising is the lack of records in the south-west and north-west of the County, since colonies occur just over the border in Devon and Somerset, for example the undercliff west of Lyme Regis. At the time of writing, we believe there to be a single, though large, colony of this hairstreak in Dorset.

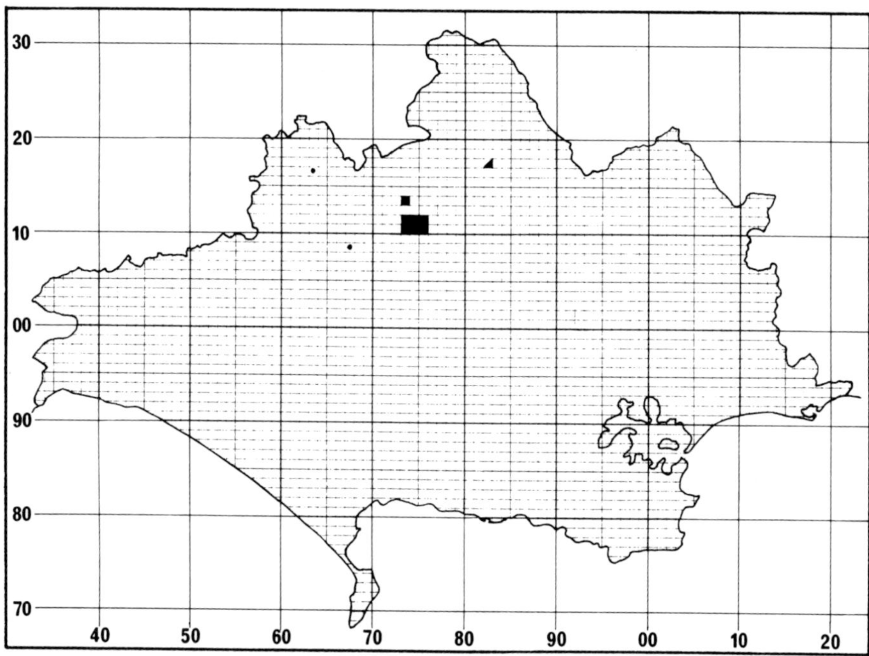

Where to see: The hedges and woods south of Lydlinch.

When to see: Females from mid August until mid September and eggs on *Prunus* twigs throughout the winter.

PURPLE HAIRSTREAK – *Quercusia quercus* Plate 22

The Purple Hairstreak is a common butterfly in Dorset woods but it is easily overlooked because the adults live most of their lives on the tree tops. It will surprise many naturalists to learn that this species is more numerous than the conspicuous Green Hairstreak and that it is the third commonest of the lycaenid butterflies (the Blues, Coppers and Hairstreaks) in the County after the Common Blue and Small Copper. It flies in mid-summer. The wings of the male are beautifully marked on the uppersides with irridescent purple. The female is predominantly black with large purple patches on the forewings. The undersides of both sexes are silver grey with an orange eye-spot near the hairstreak tail.

The eggs are laid singly on the flower buds of oak (all *Quercus* species) or on the twigs just below the buds. They are deposited all over the canopy and down to ground level on bushy trees. The small disc-shaped eggs are very easy to find during the winter, and twigs exposed to the sun should be examined. The eggs hatch at the same time as the buds break. At first the caterpillars feed on the flowers but later they rest at the bases of the leaves. Larvae can be obtained by beating, which is not to be recommended because of damage to the oaks, or by feeling the leaf bases until one of them feels squashy. The adults are less often seen because they rarely fly. When they do it is normally high up over the canopy, appearing like silver coins spinning in the sky.

Small colonies occur on isolated oaks in hedgerows or parkland, but mostly this butterfly breeds in the tree tops of copses and woods. Populations, estimated from counts of the eggs, may be huge (several thousands) in many of the oak woods of the County but the recent replacement of many of these woods by coniferous plantations must have greatly reduced the numbers of this species in Dorset. However, even in these plantations remaining cosmetic oaks or nurse trees usually have small colonies.

Distribution and Status

Every medium to large wood containing oaks and most small woods and copses in the County probably contain colonies of the Purple Hairstreak. We have examined oaks in more than 100 1 km squares in 1983-84 and failed to find eggs on only five occasions. There is little doubt that the map is incomplete but we believe that the relative abundance of the species in Dorset is well represented. The butterfly is particularly common throughout the Blackmoor Vale, in the west of the County, and around Powerstock. Other very large colonies occur throughout the woodlands of the northern and central chalk, for example in Milborne Wood. The Purple Hairstreak also occurs throughout the area of the Tertiary soils of the Poole Basin, where, although ubiquitous, densities were much lower in 1983-84 than elsewhere. We do not know whether this is true of every year.

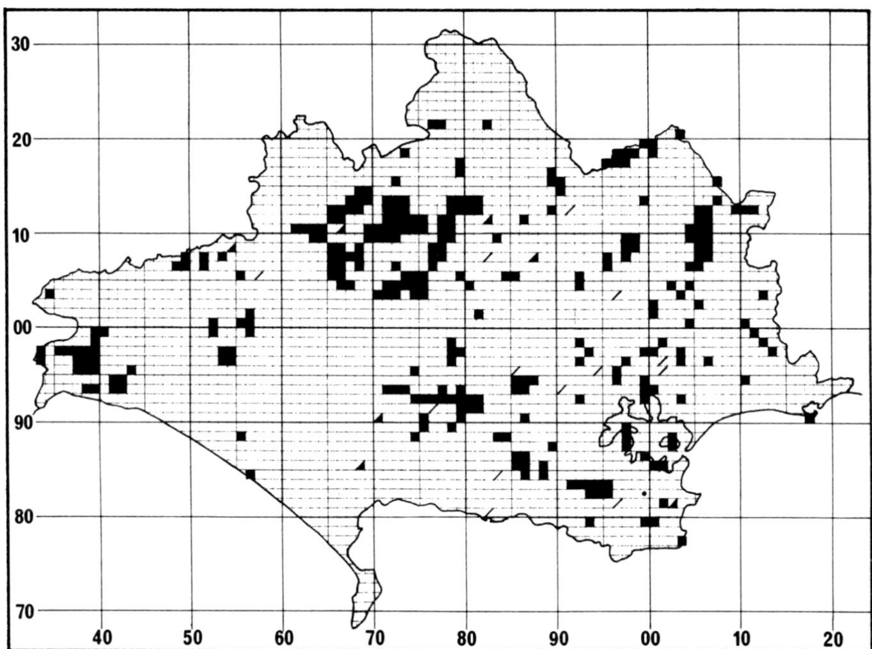

Where to see: Any wood containing oak. This species is a certainty in large oakwoods in the west, in the Blackmoor Vale and on the northern and central chalk.

When to see: Adults in mid-summer; search for the eggs during the winter and larvae in early June.

WHITE-LETTER HAIRSTREAK – *Strymonidia w-album* Plate 19

Until recently, colonies of the White-letter Hairstreak could be found throughout Dorset. However, it is the most elusive of the County's butterflies and many naturalists have been unaware of colonies even on their doorsteps. In the last decade most colonies have become extinct through the loss of the larval food plant, Elm trees.

In Dorset, as elsewhere, a colony is very small; most probably consist of no more than 20 to 50 adults. The adults seldom leave their breeding sites and spend most of their lives perched on the treetops basking or drinking honeydew. Periodically an adult will sally from the canopy in a rapid looping flight; occasionally, it will descend to feed at bramble or other flowers. Many entomologists consider the Wych Elm to be the only tree used, but the English Elm and its hybrids are equally suitable, and several colonies bred on these in Dorset. The usual habitat is a large bushy tree, although smaller specimens may be used. However, elm hedges and young suckers are unsuitable. The most important feature is that the tree should be large enough to flower, since the larvae hatch in early April before leafbreak, and must usually feed on the flowers before changing to the leaves. Both eggs and larvae are quite easy to find. The former look like miniature grey flying saucers afixed to flat elm buds or twigs on the sunny side of the canopy. The caterpillar is camouflaged to resemble a leaf, but can be seen from below as dark slug-like silhouettes on the leaves.

Distribution and Status

Dale considered this butterfly to be 'rare' in the 19th century and gave two localities, Bloxworth and Buckland Newton, with the inference that both were extinct. Parkinson Curtis, who knew his Hairstreaks rather better, considered this to be a harsh assessment, because in the 1960s he wrote, 'there are two well established colonies at least, carrying a good head of insects'. We believe that both authors grossly under-estimated the status of this elusive insect. The map shows post-1969 records from 76 different 1 km squares, representing at least 60 colonies, and it is certain that many more have been overlooked. Most records were supplied by experts familiar with the species (e.g. R. W. Smith) and we do not believe that these are newly-established colonies, for this is a highly sedentary species. Moreover, it is noteworthy that, in addition to the two colonies of which he had personal experience, Parkinson Curtis listed records from 19 other localities in the previous 150 years and that our incomplete records from the 1970s to 1980s include no less than 15 of these sites.

In the 1970s, colonies existed on all soils in the County, but were probably commonest on the poorly recorded northern clays, where the elm was a common hedgerow tree. There were also several colonies in Purbeck, around Wimborne, and between Dorchester and Weymouth. Many of these have have become extinct since Dutch elm disease. No survey has been made of the extent of this damage, but losses have been heavy and perhaps total in the Blackmoor Vale, on the northern Chalk and around Wimborne. At the time of writing, at least one colony survives in Purbeck, at Durleston, another on English elm on the central chalk and there are at least 12 on wych elms between Dorchester and Weymouth and around Beaminster (R. W. Smith). However the future of all must be in doubt.

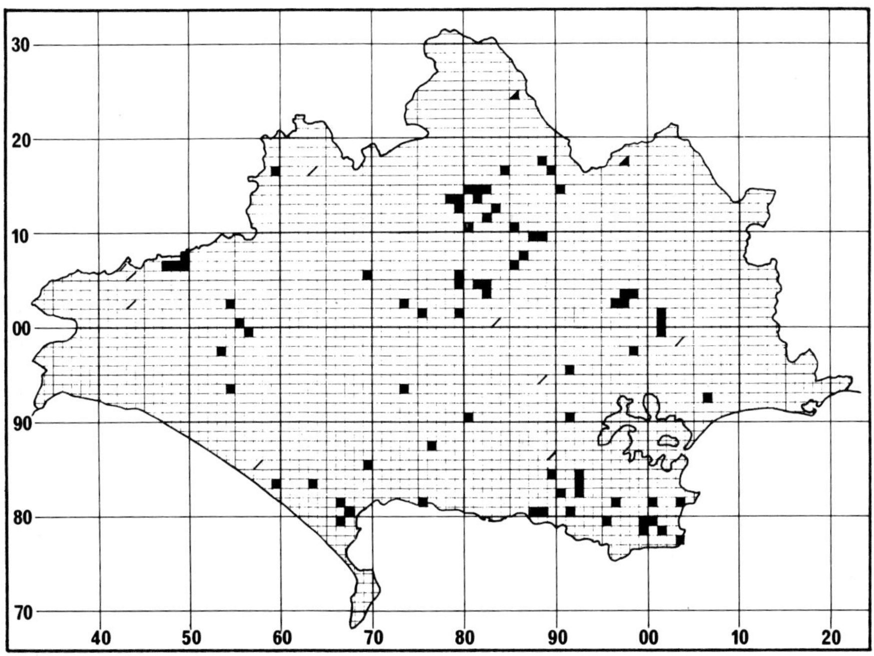

Where to see: Durleston Country Park. It is worth checking surviving elms anywhere in the County.

When to see: Like the other woodland Hairstreaks, we have no transect counts of this secretive butterfly. Adults emerge in early July and fly for about three weeks. Eggs may be found on bare twigs during the winter and full grown larvae can be found in early June.

SMALL COPPER – *Lycaena phlaeas* Plate 18

This delightful little butterfly is the second commonest lycaenid in the County and is still very well distributed on all soils. It is to be found in more or less discrete colonies. There are occasionally three, and in warm summers, four adult broods a year, but two broods is normal in Dorset. The second emergence, in high summer, is generally the larger, but even then the best colonies consist of only a few hundred adults. The early brood from most colonies is small, consisting of only a few tens of individuals. As Parkinson Curtis wrote, 'I think a collector would be hard put to it to net thirty in a day'.

Most colonies breed on rough open grassland, usually in small areas and always where the foodplant Common Sorrell (*Rumex acetosa*) and Sheep's Sorrell (*R. acetosella*) grow. The small white eggs are quite easily found at the bases of leaves, as are the slug-like caterpillars, which eat grooves in the leaves. Both Sorrells grow in rough, freshly disturbed or grazed grassland, but are shaded out of taller swards. In Dorset, Common Sorrell is very widespread, especially on chalk and heavy soils, whereas Sheep's Sorrell is slightly more local, growing mainly on acidic sandy and gravelly soils, especially in the Poole Basin and the western greensands.

Colonies of Small Coppers may be found in many situations on rough wasteland, along the coasts where erosion causes permanently open conditions, on sand dunes, in old pits and quarries on all soils, on grazed unimproved chalk and limestone downs, on open heathland, along well drained banks, along roadsides, and in open woodland. Unfortunately, various modern developments have caused a reduction in many of the suitable localities for this species. These include the increased shadiness of our woods, the general tidying up of the countryside, the reclamation of heathlands, the lack of sheep and rabbit grazing on unimproved downland, and the intensification of agriculture. Unlike most butterflies, the Small Copper and its foodplants can survive many agricultural improvements, but generally at much lower densities than formerly.

Distribution and Status

In the 19th century, Dale included the Small Copper among eleven butterflies that he described, without qualification, as 'common' and Bankes soon afterwards wrote 'generally common'. For Haines, in the first part of this century, it was 'common in fields, woods and rough places' throughout the County and Carr thought it 'pretty generally distributed' but noted that it was seldom numerous.

There is no doubt that many former colonies have disappeared since these assessments were made, for the reasons already described. The map is far from complete, especially in the Halstock and Western Vales, but the dearth of records from the flatter chalklands, stretching from west of Dorchester to Bere Regis, Blandford and north of Wimborne, reflects the scarcity or absence of colonies in most of this prairie belt. There are similar genuine gaps elsewhere, for example in the north of the Blackmoor Vale. We expect the species to decline further. Nevertheless at the time of writing, it remains a very well distributed butterfly throughout much of the County and is numerous, locally, especially on the remaining heathlands and along the coast.

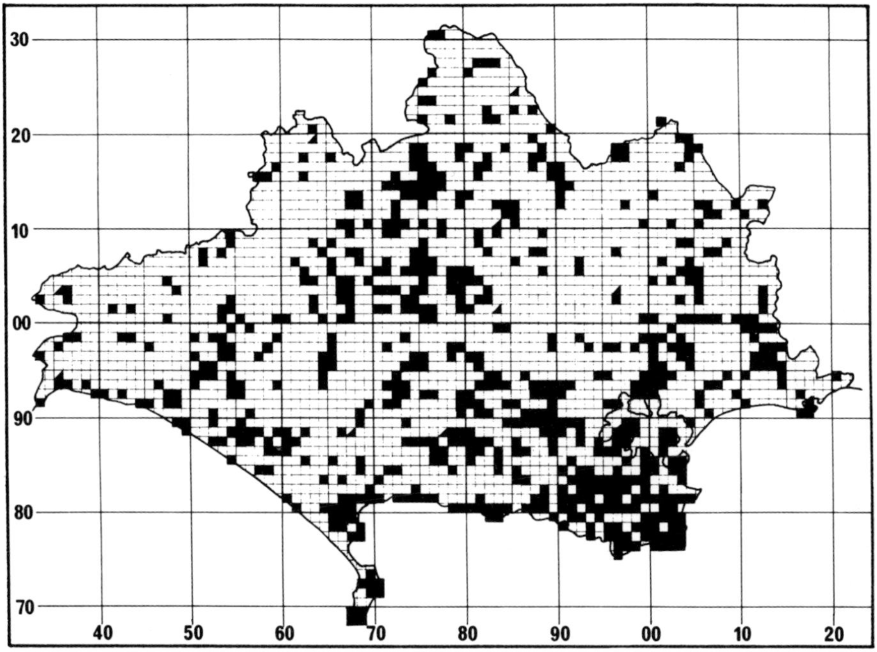

Where to see: Warm, rough grassland along the coast or on the heathlands.

When to see: The emergence of the two to three broods varied in 1976-83 and the peaks in numbers are more distinct in any one year. Usually the first brood flies in May, the larger second brood in August and in warm years, a smaller third brood in October.

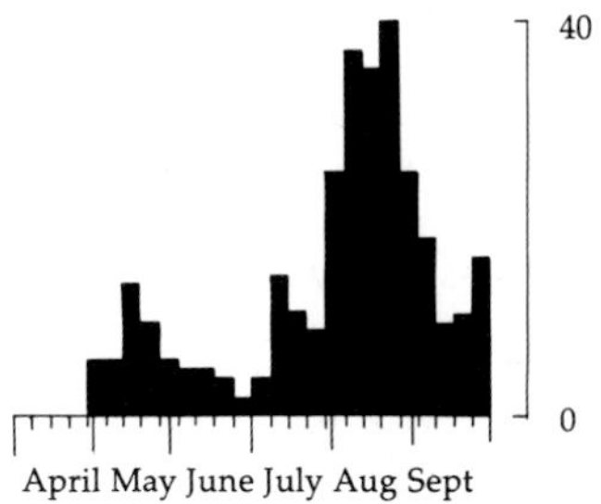

SMALL BLUE – *Cupido minimus* Plate 28

Dorset is one of the strongholds of this local and declining butterfly. As its name implies, it is the smallest of the native Blues. It is also the least conspicuous, both in appearance and behaviour. The adults fly in late spring and lay their eggs on the flowerheads of Kidney Vetch (*Anthyllis vulneraria*). These tiny, pale-blue discs are inserted between the 'fingers' of the flowerbuds. In our good colonies, scarcely a vetch head escapes being laid upon and the eggs can be found easily by parting the flowers. Often, three or four eggs occur on each flower head. The young larva enters the flower and feeds on the developing seed but is easy to find when older among the fading flowers. The pupa is formed on the ground. A few emerge as a second generation of adults in August, especially in warm years, but most hibernate until next spring.

Kidney Vetch is a local plant in Dorset, growing mainly on the chalk and limestone downs and along the coasts. The Small Blue is even more local, restricted to small discrete colonies often only a few metres in area and where the vetch grows in sunny sheltered nooks. Typical Dorset colonies breed on broken cliffs, undercliffs, hollows on the downs, abandoned chalk and lime pits and on the steep southfacing banks of roads, railways and earthworks. Open downland is rarely used in Dorset. An average sized colony consists of 20-30 adults living on a few Kidney Vetch plants. The adults fly less freely than most other Blues and are more often found perched or basking on sheltered shrubs or tall grasses. They seldom leave their colonies and thus require flowering vetch year after year on the same spot if they are to survive. Spring and summer grazing, unless very light, can be disastrous and extinctions have occurred when all of the flowerheads have been eaten. On the other hand, the short-lived vetch needs open conditions for re-establishment. This may explain why most Small Blue colonies occur in unusual spots where there are skeletal soils, scree or bare rock, and where there is little competition for the vetches. Similarly, good colonies breed on unstable land along the coast.

Distribution and Status

Dale, who knew this butterfly as the Little Blue, considered it to be 'widely distributed, but not common'. Others considered it to be locally common, especially in old chalkpits late in the 19th century, as did Parkinson Curtis in the first half of this century. A survey in 1978 showed that the Small Blue survived in 23 out of 48 old localities and 43 new ones were found. The latter were mainly in poorly visited areas, and had almost certainly been overlooked in the past. Most extinctions have occurred on downland, due to ploughing and agricultural improvements. Other losses have been caused by both a lack of, or too much, grazing. Fortunately, strong colonies still breed on at least eight nature reserves in the County.

Due to the survey, we believe the map of this butterfly to be more or less complete. The main strongholds are in the extreme south and the north-east of the County, which are both areas where Kidney Vetch is locally common. In the north-east there are fine colonies on ancient ditches and banks and in old chalk pits. There are few colonies on the central chalk but there are good colonies at several places in Purbeck, both on the chalk downs and the limestone coast. It is also very well distributed at Portland. One interesting colony occurs at Black Ven, off the calcareous soils, where Kidney Vetch grows in abundance on a warm undercliff.

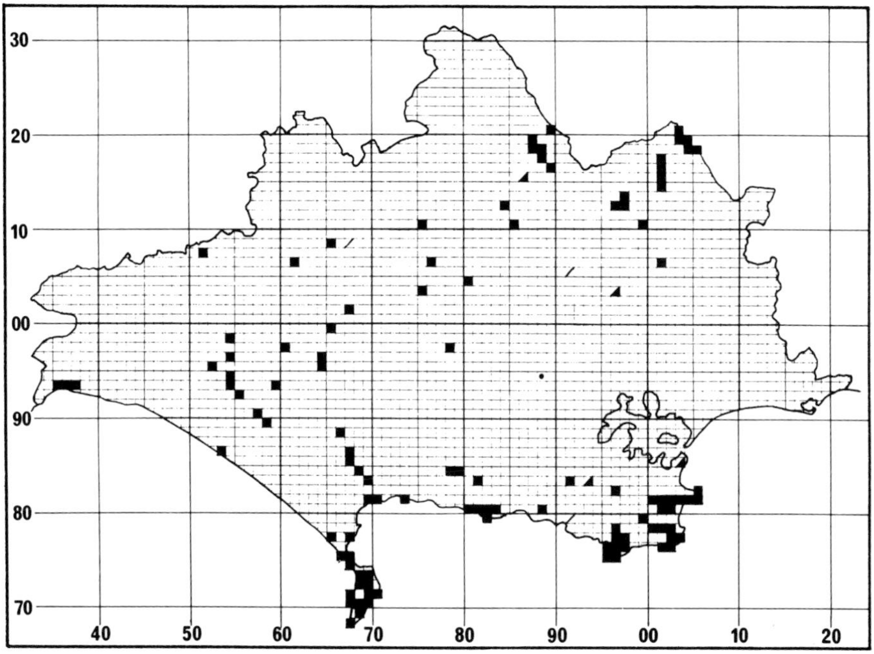

Where to see: Durleston, Portland and Black Ven.

When to see: Adults in late May and June, and as a small second brood in August. Search for eggs in June and for full grown larvae in July.

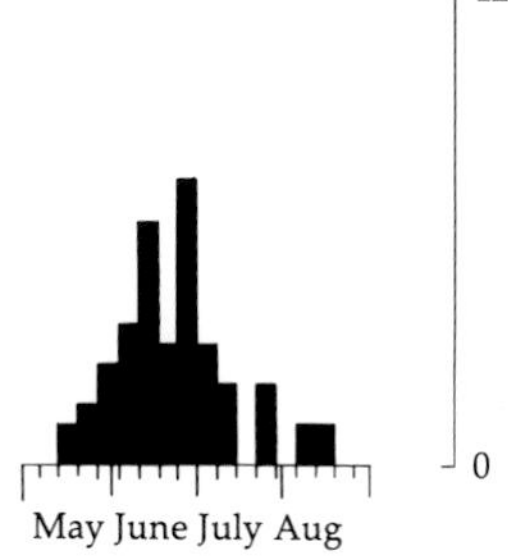

SILVER-STUDDED BLUE – *Plebejus argus* Plates 29 and 30

The Silver-studded Blue is a local and declining British butterfly. In Dorset it remains common on most heaths and our colonies, together with those in the New Forest account for the great majority of the remaining British populations.

The Silver-studded Blue occurs in self-contained colonies. These may move up to 50 metres from year to year as the quality of the habitat changes but the adults never wander far. For example in nine years of intensive observations on the chalk downs at Swanage, only a single stray male has been encountered, despite the fact that several populations consisting of thousands of individuals fly on the heathlands only 1 to 3 kilometres away.

In Dorset, as elsewhere, colonies occur in two habitats; on acid heathlands and on limestone (or very occasionally chalk) grasslands. It is now believed that these are not distinct races or subspecies but are selecting similar conditions for breeding in both types of habitat. The eggs are laid in sparse open areas. Favourite places on the heathlands are either on the young regenerating growth after a fire or on degenerate heathland where the heather canopy has opened to expose patches of bare ground. On limestone the eggs are invariably laid near bare rock or rubble, often inserted into a crack where Bird's-foot Trefoil or Rockrose abuts onto the rock. The full range of larval food plants is unknown, but is considerable, and includes gorse (*Ulex* spp.), heaths (*Erica* spp.), Ling (*Calluna vulgaris*), Bird's-foot Trefoil (*Lotus corniculatus*), and Rockrose (*Helianthemum nummularium*). There is a very close relationship with ants: wild larvae are tended by Black Ants, *Lasius alienus* or *L. niger,* and the pupa is buried in ant cells.

The best places to find the Silver-studded Blue are on those parts of the heathland which are humid and where Cross-leaved Heath (*Erica tetralix*) grows. Large populations develop also on dry heathland in the first years after a fire or cut. Some colonies may be vast, numbering tens or hundreds of thousands of individuals, making an unforgettable sight in a habitat that with the exception of the Grayling, is poor for butterflies. Colonies survive on isolated fragments of heathland so long as young growth is maintained. Most limestone colonies are in abandoned quarries and on cliffs where sparse vegetation grows between bare rock.

Distribution and Status

Colonies occur on most of the remaining heathland. There are very large populations in several parts of Purbeck, around Morden Bog, on the western heathlands and near the eastern boundary. Several colonies are on nature reserves or protected land but the others are at some risk. Many must already have been lost, but we still agree with both Dale and Parkinson Curtis that this species is 'common on all heaths'. The colonies on Portland are much smaller and more localised. They were well known to Victorian collectors and are probably of a similar status today. Most are safe unless quarrying occurs on a greater scale. Records from the Purbeck coast are not believed to refer to colonies. Recent sightings on the central chalk refer to genuine but single individuals that have been found intermittently in by H. Halahan and others. It seems likely that there is a chalk downland colony somewhere near Milton Abbas, but no one has been able to trace it. In the past, when the downs were better grazed, there were colonies on Gussage Down and at Gussage St. Michael.

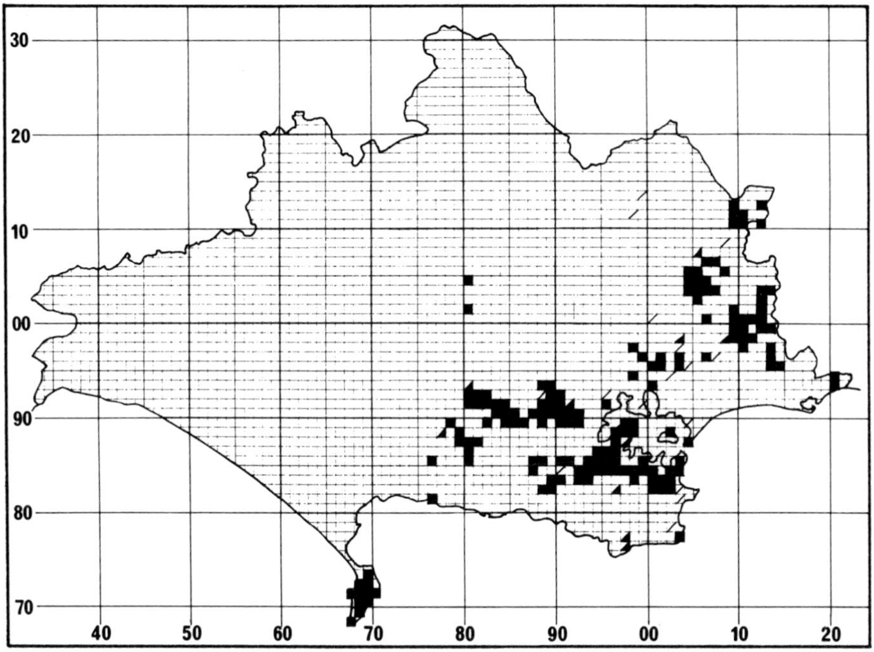

Where to see: In slightly moister areas (humid heath) or on young growth on almost all the heathlands. Abandoned quarries on Portland.

When to see: One generation a year. The emergence varies from year to year and is nothing like so long in any one year as the combined records of the histogram suggest. In most years they begin in late June and peak in mid-July.

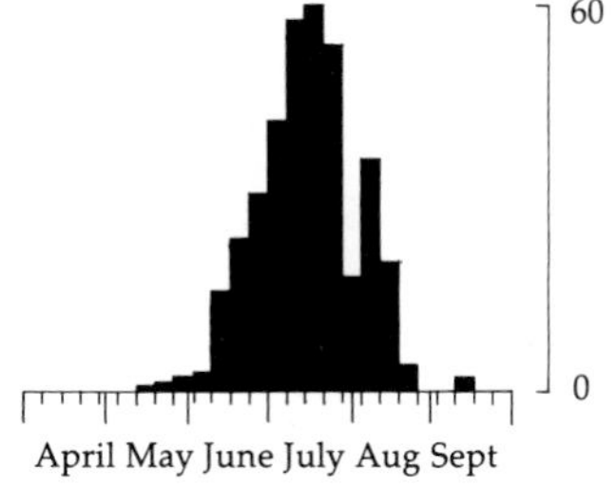

BROWN ARGUS – *Aricia agestis* Plate 25

This butterfly is locally distributed and confined to the southern half of Britain. Dorset is one of its strongholds and probably contains more colonies than any other County. The Brown Argus is sometimes confused with the brown form of the female Common Blue (which is a much commoner insect in Dorset) or, on the heathlands, with the female Silver-studded Blue. We refer naturalists to the standard textbooks for the diagnostic features of the lycaenids and merely add that, when flying, the Brown Argus appears to be coloured silver-grey, and to be very small; it is more like a Small Blue than any other species on the wing.

The Brown Argus occurs in self-contained colonies which breed on the same sites year after year, although occasionally, single adults will stray. There are two generations a year, in spring and in late summer. These fluctuate greatly in size, varying from tens to several hundreds of adults. In Dorset, most colonies breed on open calcareous (especially chalk) grassland, where the caterpillars feed on Common Rockrose (*Helianthemum nummularium*), and where they are invariably tended by ants. The preferred localities are mainly on warm south facing slopes of steep downland that are regularly grazed. They are also found on the thin soils of chalk banks and abandoned pits. In recent years many colonies have been lost because Rockrose has been eliminated from many downs by agricultural improvements and by the cessation of rabbit and sheep grazing. A few colonies exist, mainly in woods, on the gentler chalk slopes and on the heathlands and rough places in Purbeck. Some of the latter breed on Rockrose growing on chalk rubble laid as ballast, others are believed to use Common Storksbill (*Erodium cicutarium*) or species of *Geranium* as the foodplant.

Distribution and Status

Dale described the Brown Argus as 'widely distributed' in 19th century Dorset, and Haines called it 'locally common' early this century, a description with which Parkinson Curtis agreed 50 years later. Although most of Parkinson Curtis' records are from the chalk, none of these entomologists mentioned that colonies occurred mainly on chalk downs as they did with other local butterflies. Perhaps off the chalk colonies were commoner than today for example in open coppiced woodland and rough grassland where *Geranium* spp. and Common Storksbill would have been common.

Today, as is clear from the map, almost all colonies are on the chalk and show the familiar pattern of predominance on the steep, unimproved slopes of the Purbeck Hills and of the chalk stretching north-west from Eggardon to Shaftesbury and Martin. Very few colonies breed on the limestones, except on the Purbeck coast. It has been impossible to check every recent record, but we believe that very few, if any, are inaccurate. Those shown on unlikely soils include strays, as at Arne, and Parkinson Curtis' and Brown's old records around Parkstone; others are genuine colonies, for example near Studland and Furzebrook. There have undoubtably been numerous extinctions throughout the range in the County, but the species remains a locally common butterfly.

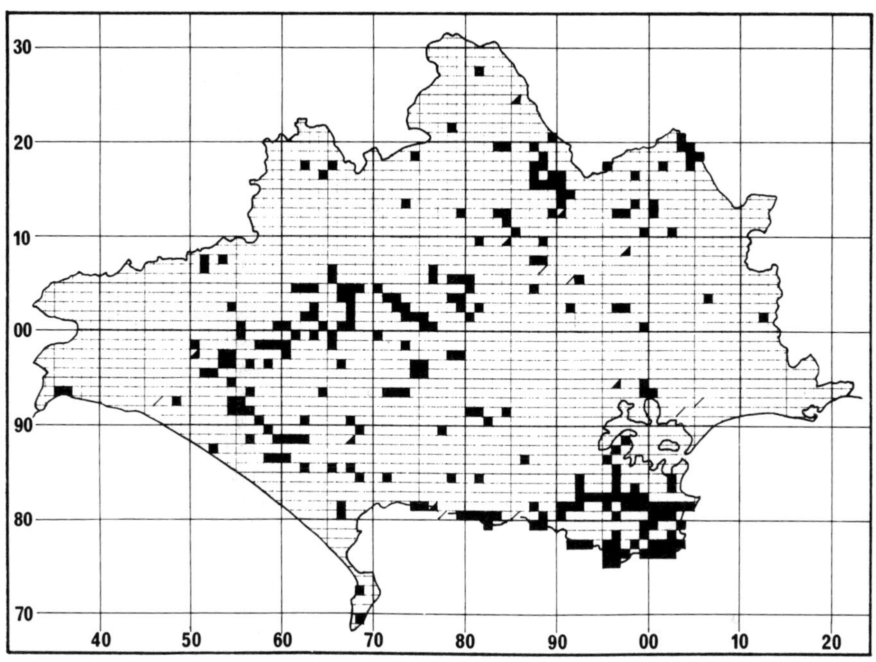

Where to see: South facing slopes of the Purbeck Hills; Hod Hill; most unimproved downs in the north.

When to see: The first brood emerges in early to mid May in most years, reaching a peak towards the end of the month. The second brood has a peak in late July.

160
0
April May June July Aug Sept

COMMON BLUE – *Polyommatus icarus* Plate 31

This aptly-named butterfly is the commonest lycaenid in the County. It breeds in numerous little colonies on small pockets of rough land. Most colonies consist of fewer than a hundred adults in contrast to the thousands of individuals in some Dorset populations of Chalkhill and Adonis Blues. The Common Blue is predominantly a sedentary butterfly and lives in discrete colonies, however, the adults are more prone to wander than most other species of Blue.

The main foodplant is Bird's-foot Trefoil (*Lotus corniculatus*), but on the heavier soils, the Marsh Bird's-foot Trefoil (*L. uliginosus*) is used, as, occasionally are other leguminous plants. The egg is a white disc laid on the tender leaflets, and is very easy to find. The caterpillar is pale green and is well camouflaged. Its presence is usually betrayed by ants drinking its sweet secretions. In Dorset, the red ant *Myrmica sabuleti* and the black ant *Lasius alienus* have been observed attending the Common blue, but we suspect that other species of ant protect the caterpillars on the heavier soils.

The best colonies are where the trefoil grows tall and bushy on eroding cliffs, undercliffs, wasteland, abandoned quarries and pits, and flowery unimproved chalk and limestone downlands. Smaller colonies may be found where the foodplant grows in woodland rides and young coppice, across the heaths, and on well-drained hedgerow banks. In swampy areas the tops of ant mounds may be used.

Parkinson Curtis found that in the wing colouring of females tended to be bluer in wet habitats or in localities with high rainfall or sea mists and browner elsewhere. The highest percentages of blue females was in 'moist lush little valleys of the heathland', on Portland and in west Dorset. Without a thorough study, we agree, and would add the Blackmoor Vale and Purbeck Hills to the list of localities where the females are most blue.

Distribution and Status

Dale describes the species as 'common' in the 19th century but Parkinson Curtis qualified this with 'usually common in places not definitely under cultivation provided its foodplants are available'. This is even truer now and reflects the loss of Bird's-foot Trefoil from modern improved fields and its reduction in most natural grassland since the cessation of rabbit grazing. Nevertheless it remains one of the commonest plants in the County and the Common Blue, although greatly diminished, is still one of the commonest butterflies. The map is far from complete, especially in the west.

Today fine colonies breed along almost all the coastline, except Chesil and at Bournemouth. It is ubiquitous along the steep, unfertilised downland of the Purbeck Hills and on the central and northern chalklands from Eggardon to Shaftesbury and Martin. Numerous smaller colonies occur throughout the County but, on the heaths, it is largely absent from the pure heather areas. There is probably no wood in the County that does not have a small colony, nor abandoned quarry or wasteland that does not support a large one. Small colonies also breed along well-drained road banks and cuttings on the chalk and sands. It is probably ubiquitous at low densities on wider verges and boggy land throughout the Blackmoor Vale.

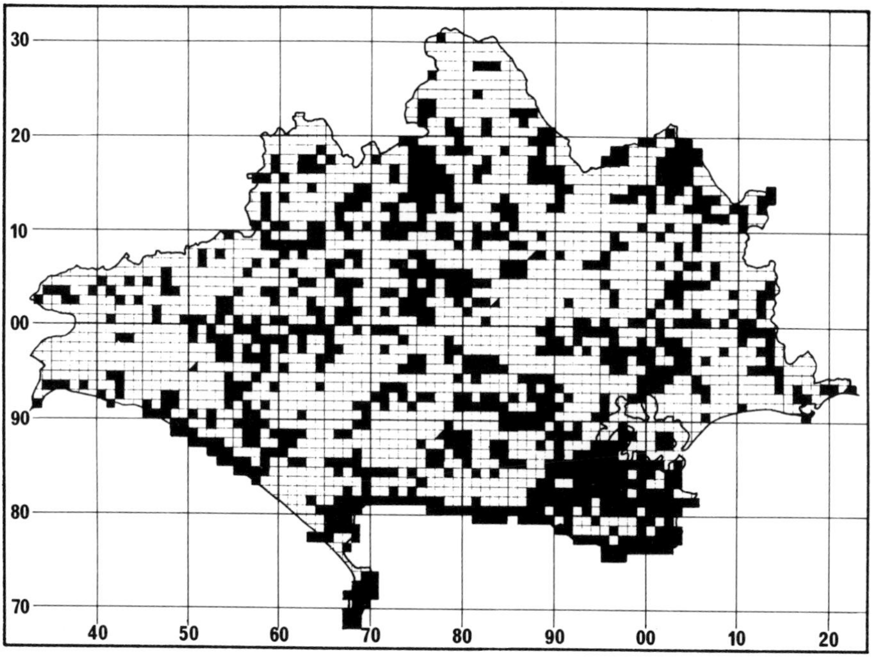

Where to see: Rough land throughout Dorset, especially the coast and flowery downs.

When to see: The first brood normally emerges in late May and reaches peak numbers in mid June. The second brood reaches its peak in late August and early September. There is sometimes a small third brood in October, not shown on the histogram.

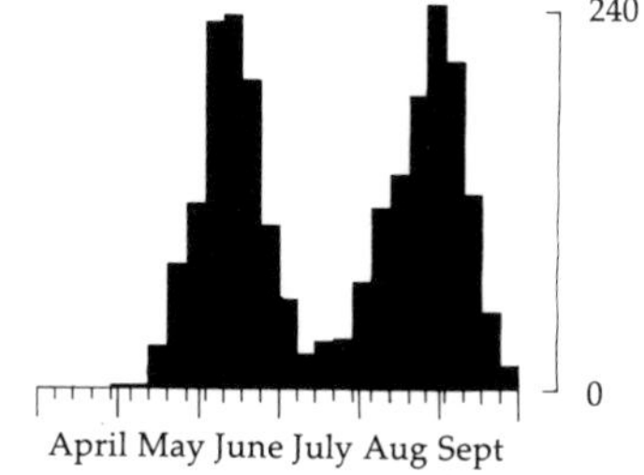

CHALKHILL BLUE – *Lysandra coridon* Plate 23

As its name implies, this beautiful Blue is confined to the chalk and limestone outcrops of Dorset, where like the Adonis Blue, its larvae feed on Horseshoe Vetch (*Hippocrepis comosa*). The adults live in discrete colonies, although very occasionally, a male will stray and will be recorded away from the chalk or limestone (see map). Colony size varies from site to site and from year to year. Sometimes, merely a handful of individuals may be seen, but at their best, the milky-blue males and duller brown females teem in tens of thousands over their breeding sites. The causes of these fluctuations are unknown, although there is some evidence that numbers generally increase in the first few years after grazing has been relaxed, when the turf grows taller and plants flower. Periodic grazing is essential on most sites otherwise Horseshoe Vetch is shaded out of the sward. In the past, very large colonies of Chalkhill Blues sometimes developed on the billiard table swards that occurred regularly when rabbits were abundant.

Like the vetch, colonies of this butterfly are commonest, but not confined to, south facing slopes of hills. It also breeds on flat ground which has survived improvement. Unlike the Adonis Blue, there is no preference when egg laying for vetches growing in a short sward. The larvae feed by night and can be found at dusk in early June, usually smothered by black, red or yellow ants which drink the sweet secretions from the caterpillar.

More than most species, colonies of Chalkhill Blues occasionally contain strangely marked individuals. Parkinson Curtis studied their occurrence in Dorset, and we refer the specialist to his manuscript.

Distribution and Status

The Chalkhill Blue must have been an extremely common species from the 15th to 18th centuries when sheep walks were extensive. By the 19th century Dale described it as being 'generally distributed and common on the chalk range', whilst in this century Parkinson Curtis considered its distribution to be 'curiously capricious ranging from complete absence from apparently likely spots to extreme abundance in special haunts'. Twenty years ago he could still write, 'the County contains many large colonies where the species is abundant'. On the other hand, he wrote of the destruction, since 1898, of many former colonies around Blandford due to urban expansion; of it being much more restricted than formerly around Cranborne due to 'improvements'; and of another site being so overgrown that the foodplant had been smothered.

Since then there have been many extinctions through agricultural improvements which have caused the loss of the foodplant. Nearly as serious has been the decline in sheep and rabbit grazing on most surviving unfertilised fragments, although unlike the Adonis Blue, the Chalkhill Blue has generally survived in taller swards so long as the foodplant persists. Despite these losses, colonies still exist on most steep unimproved downland. There are records from the Purbeck coast and Portland; on the scarp of the Purbeck Hills and westwards to Maiden Castle and Eggardon; and north-eastwards along the chalk scarp to Shaftesbury and Martin Down. In the mid 1970s many colonies were extremely large, but most are now smaller, for no obvious reason. It has largely been eliminated from the gentler chalk slopes.

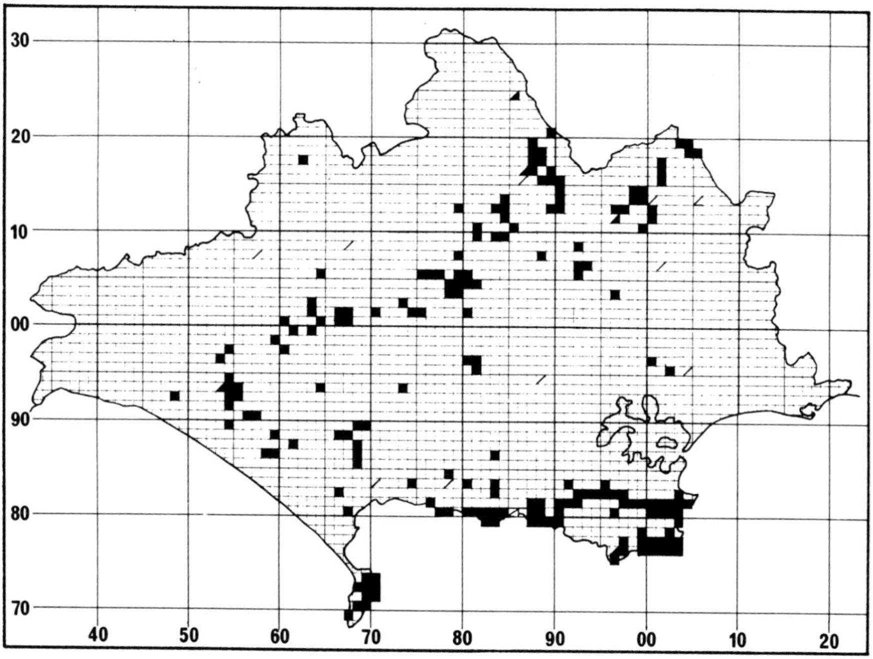

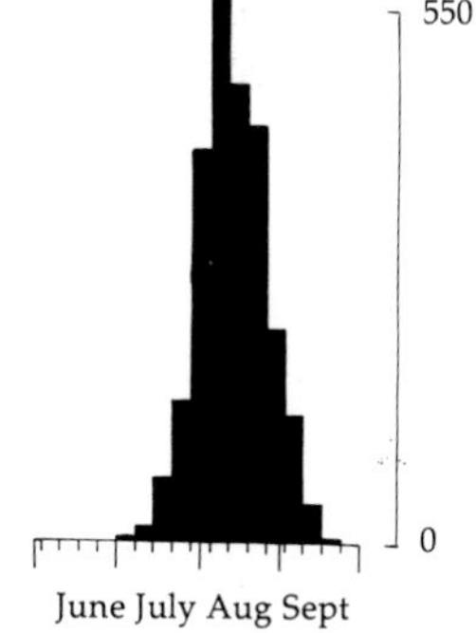

Where to see: Portland; Lulworth; Swanage, Maiden Castle, Cerne Abbas and on the steep downs south of Shaftesbury.

When to see: Mid to late July, reaching peak numbers in mid August.

ADONIS BLUE – *Lysandra bellargus* Plates 24 and 26

The Adonis Blue is a declining species in Britain and now occurs at under 100 sites. Fortunately, the decline has been rather less severe in Dorset than elsewhere, and the County is now the stronghold of this species.

The caterpillar feeds on Horseshoe Vetch (*Hippocrepis comosa*) and although colonies are restricted to the chalk and limestone grasslands, they are more locally distributed than the Vetch. These colonies are confined to warm, south-facing hillsides that are so heavily grazed that the exposed soil is baked by the sun. Occasionally they are found in a taller sward, but only if it is sparse, such as on the sides of old chalk pits. The eggs are laid beneath the leaves of Vetch plants growing in the shortest patches of turf. This means that only a few plants are used for breeding when the sward is patchy. The adults seldom stray far from their breeding sites and colonies are generally small, but if the down is well grazed and the terrain uneven, larger colonies develop. At all sites numbers fluctuate greatly from one generation to the next, regardless of the relative size of the colony.

The caterpillars are beautifully camouflaged and feed by day on the leaves of the Vetch. They can be found easily since their presence is betrayed by ants which invariably tend them, milking their sweet secretions. Such larvae may be occasionally hidden beneath a mass of 20-30 black or red ants.

Distribution and Status

Dale described the Adonis Blue as 'local' in Dorset in the 19th century, whilst Parkinson Curtis, writing in the early 1960s considered it to be 'practically coincident in range with (the Chalkhill Blue) but . . . more restricted as to the number of individuals, and of late . . . less abundant'. Surveys in 1973 and 1978 revealed that it had become extinct in about two-thirds of its former sites and that most of the remaining colonies were very small. A few sites had been destroyed by ploughing or similar agricultural changes but most had simply become too overgrown for the butterfly. Most of these sites had been abandoned as sheepwalks many years ago but a suitable sward had been maintained by rabbits until these were wiped out in the 1950s. For 25 years there was a continual loss of colonies but then restocking of the downs and the partial return of rabbits reversed the trend in the 1980s. Where colonies have survived, there has been an expansion onto neighbouring land. For example, in 1984, the once famous site of Hod Hill was recolonised from the nearby colony of Hambledon and the butterfly reappeared near Cheselbourne and in several other parts of the County. Though most welcome, we expect this to be a temporary phenomenon and that the Adonis Blue will continue to decline.

Because of the surveys, we consider the distribution maps to be virtually complete. Colonies are well distributed along the chalk scarp from Shaftesbury south-westwards to Eggardon and Litton Cheney and then eastwards to Swanage. They are also widely distributed on limestone grassland on the Purbeck coast and Portland. However, this gives an exaggerated impression of its present abundance; several colonies lie at the intersections of several grid squares, and most of those on the central chalk, such as Bulbarrow and Delcombe, became extinct in the 1970s. At present, surviving colonies in the north-east are small; much larger ones flourish on the southern chalk, especially on the south slopes of the Purbeck Hills east of Corfe Castle and on the coastal limestones.

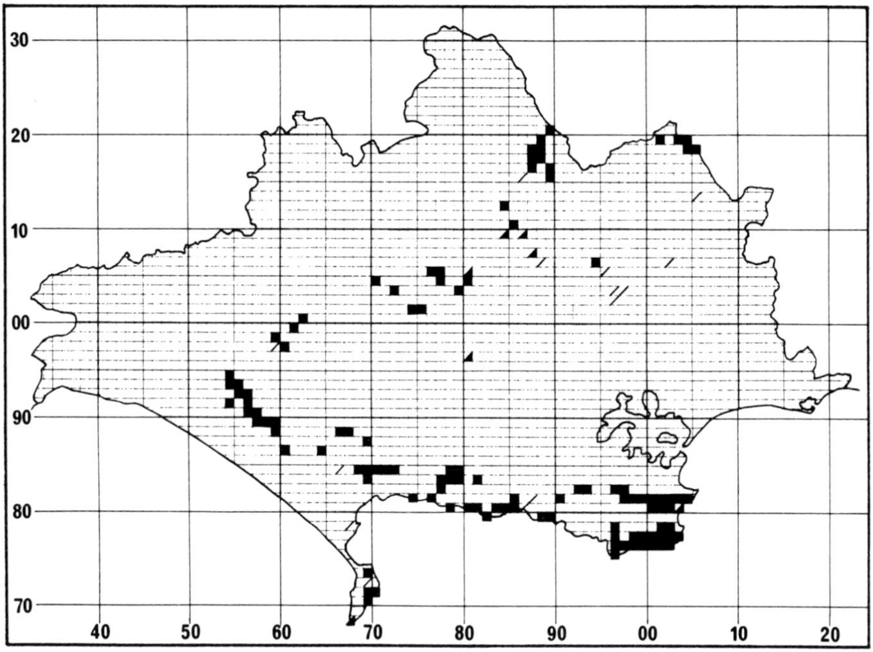

Where to see: Downland east of Corfe Castle, especially near Swanage; Durleston, Maiden Castle and Portland.

When to see: Adults in late spring and late summer. Eggs in June and September, larvae in April and late July.

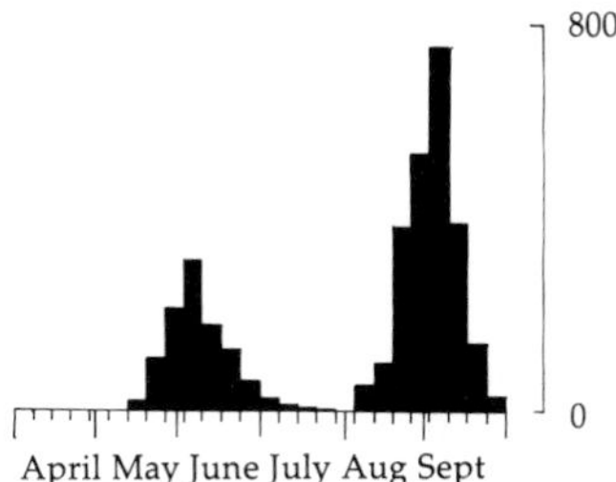

HOLLY BLUE – *Celastrina argiolus* Plate 27

The Holly Blue overwinters as a chrysalid and is the earliest Blue to emerge. In Dorset it may be seen in April in a warm spring and is out a good month before the first Common Blue although normally these two species overlap. There is a second, usually larger, brood in high summer. The wings of the male resemble a Common Blue on the uppersides, although they lack any tinge of purple. The females are more easily distinguished: the uppersides have a blue ground colour with inky black wingtips. These markings are especially pronounced in the second brood. Even more distinctive are the underwings; in both sexes they are silver-blue with an array of tiny black spots.

The Holly Blue lays its eggs singly on the flowerheads of shrubs. Holly (*Ilex aquifolium*) is generally used in the spring and Ivy (*Hedera helix*) by the second generation, although several alterntive shrubs may be used, including Gorse (*Ulex europaeus*), Dogwood (*Thelycrania sanguinea*), Spindle (*Euonymus europaeus*), Alder Buckthorn (*Frangula alnus*) and, in gardens, Snowberry (*Symphoricarpos albus*). The caterpillars feed on the flowers or berries, and occasionally the leaves. As might be expected from these food plants, this is the only species of Blue in the County that is not characteristic of open grassland or heathland. Instead it breeds along hedgerows, woodland edges and rides, in open scrub and very often in gardens. Cultivated varieties of holly and ivy are as acceptable as the native species, if they are allowed to flower and fruit. The Holly Blue is the commonest Blue to be seen in parks, gardens and urban areas, and is one of the few butterflies to breed in these habitats. Probably the largest numbers occur in mature bushy gardens and parks or the occasional patches of old woodland where there is a dense understory of holly. Yet generally even in these habitats only single individuals are seen and in some years the butterfly is rare. The Holly Blue does not form discrete colonies, even in areas where the same bushes are used year after year. It is one of our most mobile butterflies and individuals wander through town and countryside, flying along lanes and hedges.

Distribution and Status

Dale described the Holly Blue as being 'generally distributed but scarce or entirely absent in some seasons' in Dorset in the 19th century. There seems to have been little change. Parkinson Curtis accepted this description for the 20th century, although he said that it was never entirely absent, just very low in numbers some years. We agree with his assessment. During the mid-1970s numbers were relatively high and again in 1983-84. Even so, nearly all records are of single adults. The map illustrates the comparative sparsity of this butterfly fairly well and also shows its widespread distribution on all soils. However, given time, one could probably record this mobile butterfly in every garden and wood, and along every hedgerow in the County.

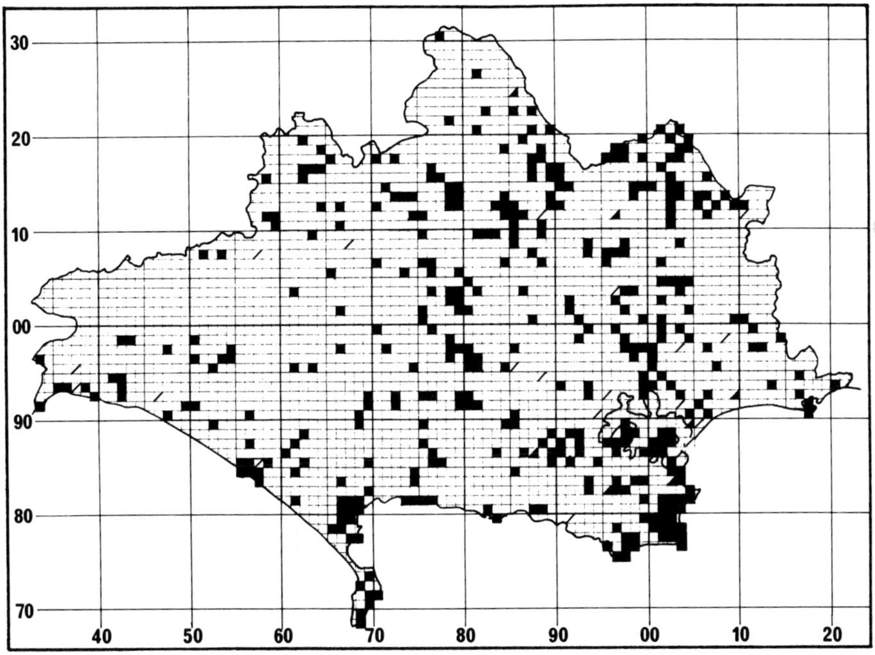

Where to see: Around flowering holly in the spring, especially in mature gardens and woods.

When to see: The only Blue flying in April or early May, peaking in mid-May in the first brood. The second brood is usually larger and reaches a peak in August.

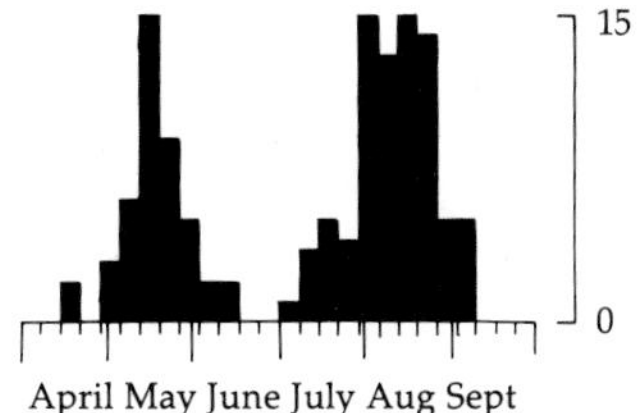

DUKE OF BURGUNDY – *Hamearis lucina* Plate 32

This springtime butterfly is one of the most rapidly declining species in the County. It lives in small discrete colonies of fewer than 50 adults, although much larger colonies have been recorded in the recent past. Colonies are found in two distinct situations; in sheltered scrubby grassland on chalk and in recent clearings and rides in woods. In both cases, the breeding area is usually small and, in woodlands, colonies move from time to time as clearings become overgrown and new ones appear. However, it is not a mobile butterfly, and once lost from an isolated wood or down, is unlikely to re-appear unless artificially introduced.

The females lay their eggs beneath the leaves of Cowslip (*Primula veris*) or, in a few woods, on Primrose (*P. vulgaris*), which the caterpillars later eat. Although both plants are widespread, breeding is restricted to particular situations. On scrubby chalk, the eggs are laid on large, partly exposed Cowslips growing in sheltered, warm places and half-shaded beneath shrubs or by taller grass. Small-leaved plants in open grassland are rejected. In woods, large-leaved Primroses, growing in sunny clearings where the ground flora has begun to grow up are selected, but neither well-shaded plants nor small-leaved clumps in full sunshine are used. In the past, suitable habitat was created year after year in coppiced woods, especially on the chalk. The decline in coppicing in Dorset is responsible for most of the extinctions. On the downs the difficult balance of succession must be maintained. Heavy grazing can eliminate a colony, yet some regeneration of breeding sites is essential, if they are not to become overgrown. Losses have occurred for both reasons.

Distribution and Status

The Duke of Burgundy has always been locally distributed in Dorset, although probably much overlooked. Dale, writing in 1886, stated that it was 'scarce and local' and had not been seen at Glanville's Wootton or Middlemarsh since 1842 (ancient specimens from these localities survive in mint condition in the Hope Museum at Oxford). Bankes agreed, but Haines early this century thought it was extending its range. If true, the increase was short lived and was soon replaced by a sharp decline. By the early 1960s Parkinson Curtis already considered it to be 'excessively local' although he knew of three large colonies where he could 'by assiduity procure a number . . . that if stated might be deemed to be a gross exaggeration'.

It is clear from the map that colonies were once well distributed on all soils in Dorset, but were frequent only in the belt of woods on the chalk, extending north-eastwards from Milton Abbas through Cranborne Chase and into Wiltshire. Despite the many extinctions, we still have post 1969 records from 31 different 1 km squares, representing perhaps 20 colonies. Many sites were surveyed by W. G. Shreeves and C. J. Tubb in 1984. Perhaps half the post 1969 colonies have already disappeared and, with around 10 remaining colonies, the Duke of Burgundy is one of the most endangered butterflies in the County, and probably dependent on nature reserves (Powestock, Fontmell and Martin Down) for its survival. Elsewhere, one or two small colonies survive towards the west and the butterfly exists in very small numbers in hollows and clearings in several of the woods on Cranborne Chase. It is probably now extinct in the woods on the chalk in the south-west of the Chase, around Wimborne, in Purbeck and in the Poole Basin.

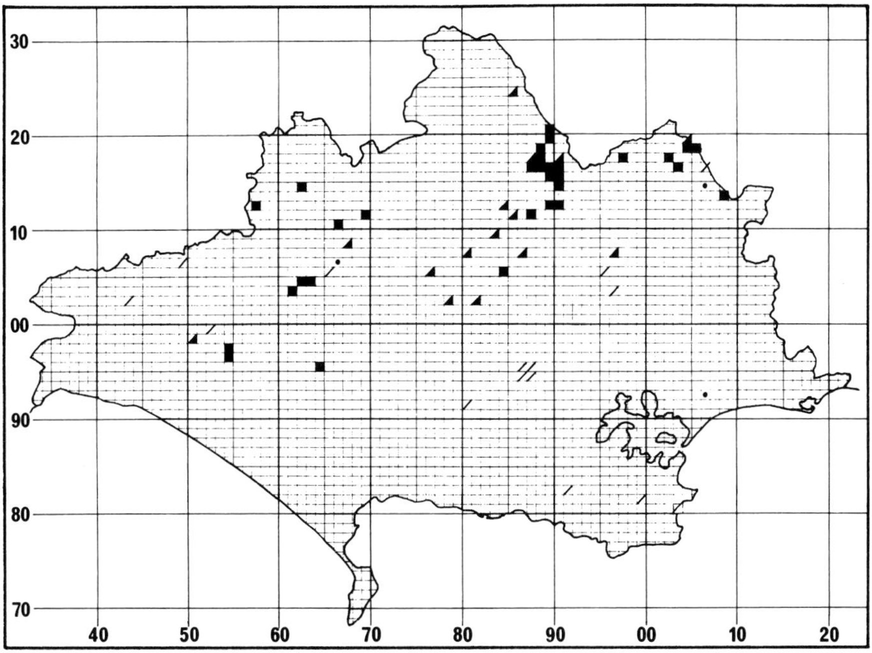

Where to see: From public footpaths at Powerstock and Fontmell Down. Do not catch under any circumstances.

When to see: There is one short brood of adults which generally reaches a peak in the second half of May. The conspicuous eggs may be found on suitable plants in June.

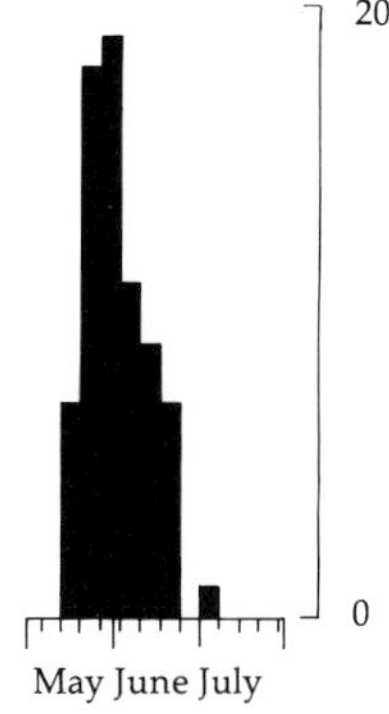

WHITE ADMIRAL – *Ladoga camilla* Plate 34

This beautiful woodland butterfly is one of the few species to have increased in Dorset during this century. At present, it is commoner than at any time since J. C. Dale began his *Entomological Journal* in 1808, and it now breeds in most larger woods, and is rare only in the western third of the County. It has a graceful, though rapid, gliding flight and is usually seen soaring high among the tree tops. Sometimes an individual descends to feed on bramble blossom in glades and rides but as a rule the White Admiral remains in the canopy, feeding on aphid honey dew. Most populations of the White Admiral are comparatively small and it is unusual to see more than two or three together.

The eggs are laid, often near to the ground, on the larval foodplant, Honeysuckle (*Lonicera periclymenum*): thin spindly plants, growing in dappled shade in rides and glades of woods are preferred. The larva hatches in the late summer. It feeds on the leaf, beginning at the tip and nibbling the blade at right angles to leave the midrib. This characteristic damage is easy to spot on suitable plants and many of the records mapped were made in this way. After a month it spins the remaining part of the leaf into a hibernation nest, from which it emerges in the spring to resume feeding. Because of its breeding habits, the White Admiral is generally found in large woods where the ground flora is fairly well shaded. Most modern woods are of this type and this explains the prosperity of this species; Victorian coppices were much too open and sunny but have gradually become more suitable during this century. Dense mature conifer plantations are too shaded and generally lack honeysuckle but small populations sometimes breed at the edges and along rides. Most Dorset colonies occur in old deciduous woodland that was once coppice with standards.

Distribution and Status

In the 19th century the White Admiral was recorded from only Cranborne, Bere Regis, Gussage St. Michael and Studland and never regularly or in large numbers. Nationally, the White Admiral spread from the New Forest and a few other strongholds in the warm summers of the 1930s and 1940s. In Dorset, expansion was earlier and continued for longer – indeed, it still seems to be spreading into the west. Thus Haines wrote that from 1913 to 1923 (when he left the County), it was steadily increasing and Parkinson Curtis listed 47 new localities in the next four decades. Nevertheless, writing in the mid 1960s, he considered it to be still 'extremely local but not uncommon in a few favoured localities . . . it should be noted what a number of records are for at most two or three specimens, since the numerous localities listed give an erroneous impression of abundance'.

Today, we have recent records from 204 1 km squares, representing around 100 distinct localities. Even so the map is probably incomplete. Most of the new localities are in the central third of the County, whereas most records from before 1960 were in the east; for example Parkinson Curtis gave just one locality in the Blackmoor Vale, yet these woods are its current stronghold. It is possible therefore, that the entire western sector of the County may be colonised in the next few decades. However, many woods may be passing their peak for White Admiral and may have become too shady.

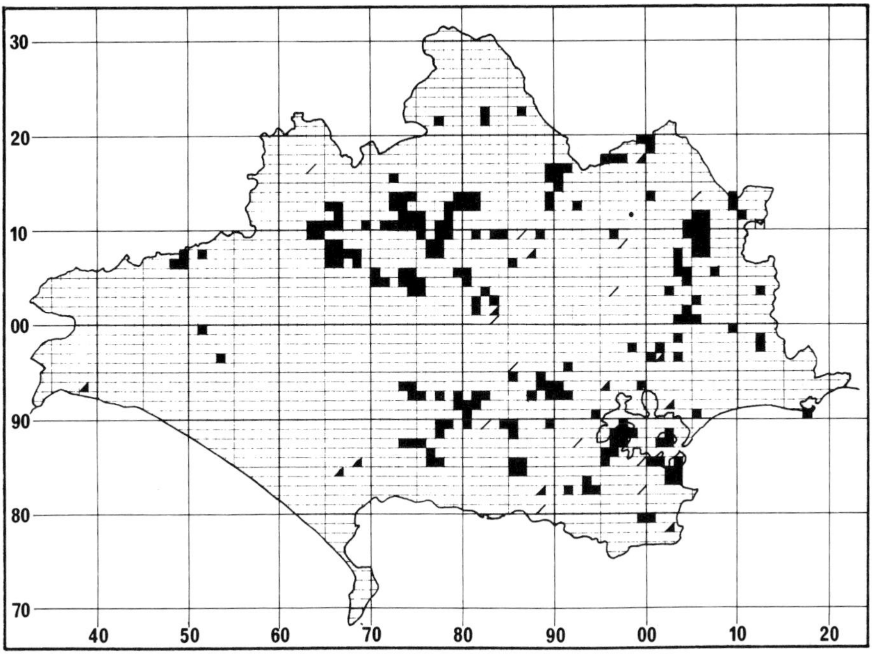

Where to see: Almost any large semi-shaded deciduous wood except in the western third of the County or in most large plantations. Ubiquitous in suitable woods in the Blackmoor Vale.

When to see: There is one generation a year, emerging in late June and reaching a peak in mid July. Then search for young larvae in late July and August and for hibernation nests (*hibernacula*) during the winter when most other leaves have been shed.

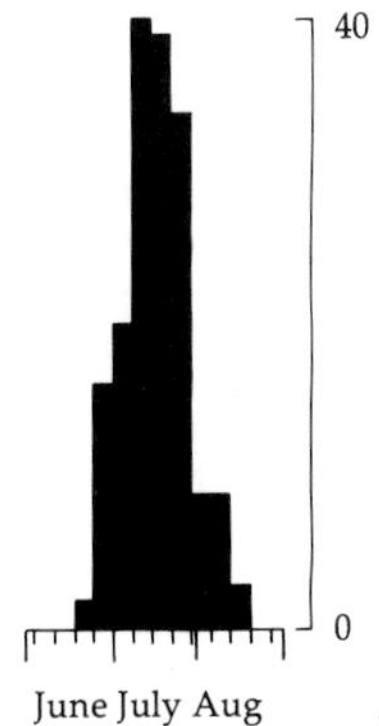

PURPLE EMPEROR – *Apatura iris* Plate 33

Despite its size and spectacular markings, the Purple Emperor is an elusive butterfly. It is more widely distributed in southern England than is generally realised but it is often overlooked as it spends most of its adult life among the tree tops. It is a genuine rarity in Dorset and only one definite colony is known. This is because, like the Brown Hairstreak, it is a butterfly of extensive woodlands, especially on those heavy soils and it is more likely to be seen in the neighbouring counties.

The larva of the Purple Emperor feeds on the leaves of the two Sallows, *Salix caprea* and *S. cinerea*. The eggs are laid singly on the uppersides of the Sallow leaves and, with practice, are quite easy to find, although many are laid above head height. Each is usually laid on a half-shaded leaf, within the body of a slightly prominent, medium-sized Sallow, growing on the edge of a ride or clearing. It hatches after about a fortnight, and the larva hibernates when fairly small, hidden in a fork or a scar on a twig. When fully fed, next June, it moults into a beautifully camouflaged pupa resembling a Sallow leaf.

A colony of the Purple Emperor usually covers a large area and the eggs are scattered on suitable Sallows in several neighbouring woods. The breeding ground is a discrete entity that is used by a self-contained colony year after year, and adults seldom stray far. On emerging, adults gather to mate on the top of a prominent 'master tree', usually on a hill top. The males battle with each other, soaring above the canopy in spectacular, fast, circling flights, with their wings flashing deep purple whenever they catch the sun. This is the best time to see this butterfly. Sometimes the odd individual will descend to drink sap, carrion, dung, or at puddles, but most of their lives are spent perched out of sight on tree tops, drinking honeydew. The female is seen less frequently than the male. She flies rarely, except to reach Sallows, and is then extremely secretive, flying rapidly in light and shade between the branches of trees.

Distribution and Status

The maps shows that the Purple Emperor has been reported from at least 19 different 1 km squares during the last 150 years. Some of these records may be mistakes, since it is common for inexperienced observers to confuse highflying White Admirals for the Purple Emperor. On the other hand, a few genuine sites may have been overlooked. In the 19th century, Dale considered the Purple Emperor to be 'very rare'. Parkinson Curtis, writing more recently, held much the same view but he also thought that some localities for the species may have been overlooked.

There are authentic records of Purple Emperor from several areas of Dorset, although most are of single sightings. These records are from woods on all types of soil and it is possible, although unlikely, that some with old records still have colonies. The only breeding colony known to us is in private woodland, not open to the public, on Cranborne Chase. There is a number of records from the vicinity of Horton, and although breeding has not been confirmed, sightings are regular enough to make it likely that these are not strays from colonies in the New Forest but represent a second colony.

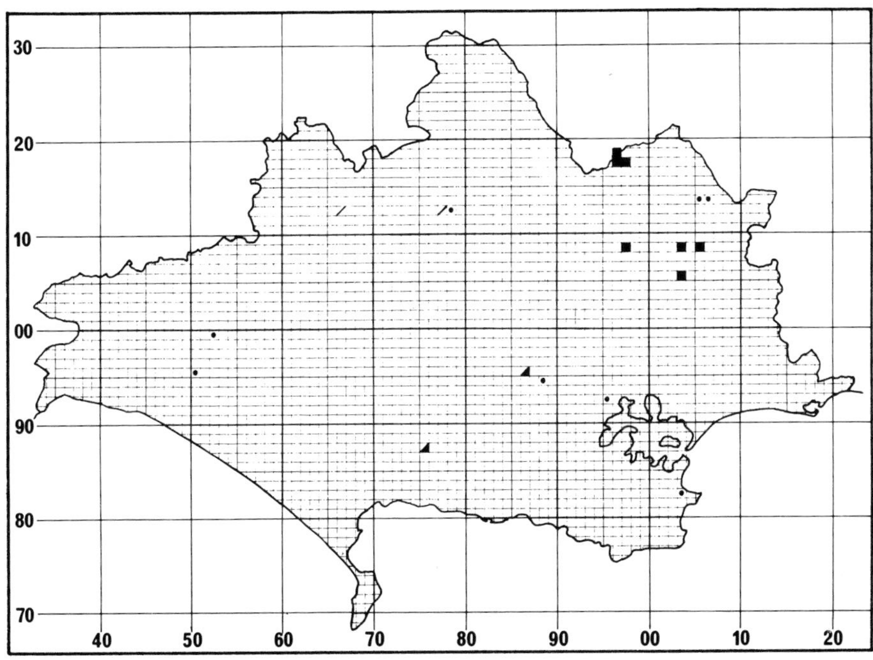

Where to see: Not in Dorset. Good colonies breed on several nature reserves in Wiltshire, Hampshire, Sussex and Buckinghamshire.

When to see: Look for the adults throughout July and early August. The eggs may be found in late July and August.

RED ADMIRAL – *Vanessa atalanta* Plate 38

This large and strikingly beautifully butterfly may be seen anywhere in the County in the late summer and autumn. It varies in abundance from being quite scarce in some years to very common in others. These fluctuations are explained by the fact that the Red Admiral is a migrant. It flies northwards from southern Europe, where it can survive in the warm winters, to reach the Dorset coast in spring and early summer. Immigration is seldom seen, although J. S. Ash and M. D. Crosby describe its arrival at Portland in 1956 (*Dorset Proceedings*, Vol 78, page 33). The immigrants spread throughout Dorset (and Britain) to lay their eggs singly on Nettle leaves (*Urtica* spp.) and occasionally on Hop (*Humulus lupulus*). The caterpillars feed on the leaves and produce a larger number of adults in the late summer. These home bred adults may produce a further generation in the autumn. Unlike the Painted Lady and Clouded Yellow, the pattern of generations is not clear from the transect counts (see opposite). Instead, numbers build up during the season and last well into October. The regular arrival of immigrants over a long period probably accounts for the lack of a distinct pattern of generations. There is some evidence of a return migration in the autumn, but probably most individuals attempt to hibernate. Few survive our cold winters, although successful individuals are occasionally seen in the very early spring. It is not believed that such survivors contribute greatly to the Dorset populations, which depend almost entirely on immigration each year. Adults may be seen anywhere in the County, but have a partiality for wooded or sheltered areas, and are a familiar sight on garden flowers. The Red Admiral is also attracted by rotting fruit, and is often seen in some numbers sucking windfalls beneath apple and plum trees.

Distribution and Status

In most years, the Red Admiral is common and widely distributed throughout the County. Parkinson Curtis noticed no difference in numbers on the different soils and altitudes. Our experience is similar, and the map therefore has little significance except to reflect the relative numbers of recent reports of the Red Admiral compared with other highly mobile and ubiquitous species, such as the Peacock, Small Tortoiseshell, Large and Small Whites, and other migrants. There is no evidence to suggest that the status of the Red Admiral has changed since the early 19th century, when Dale described it simply as common.

Nevertheless, all authors have noticed that the Red Admiral varies considerably in numbers from year to year, ranging from 'always some' to 'common' (Haines and Parkinson Curtis). Despite fluctuations, the Red Admiral had usually occurred in greater numbers than any other migratory butterfly. This was also true of 1976-83, except in 1983 when it was exceeded by the Clouded Yellow. Combined counts by the annual Butterfly Monitoring Scheme at Swanage and Studland for all years are 211 Red Admiral : 127 Clouded Yellow (88% of which occured in 1983) : 54 Painted Lady – a ratio of roughly four to two to one. It should be noted that all three migrants continue to fly in October after counting has ceased, but this is thought not to distort the relative figures.

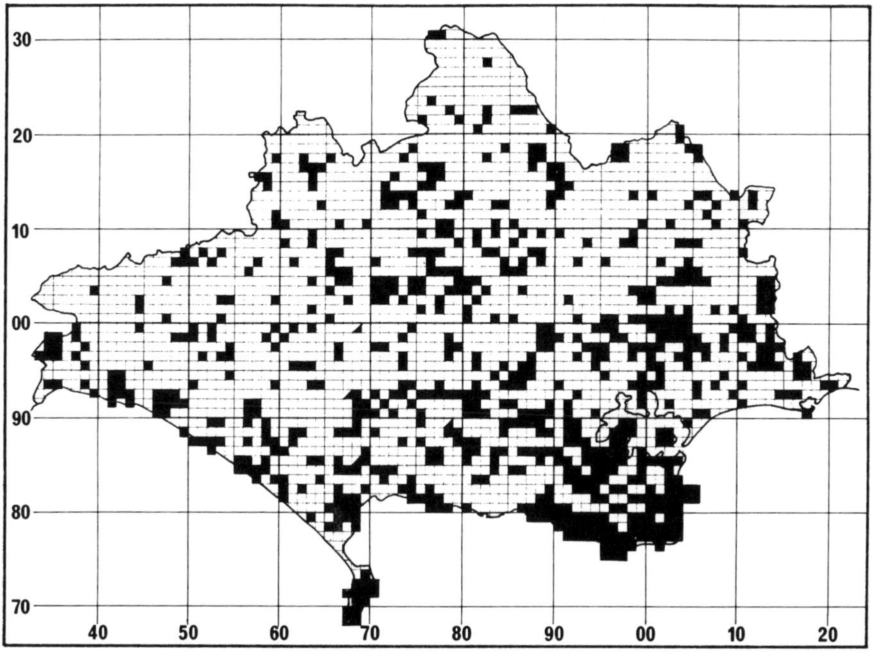

Where to see: On flowers and fruit, often in gardens and orchards.

When to see: Very occasionally in spring, but seldom before June; then in increasing numbers reaching a peak in early September, and often continuing in good numbers into October.

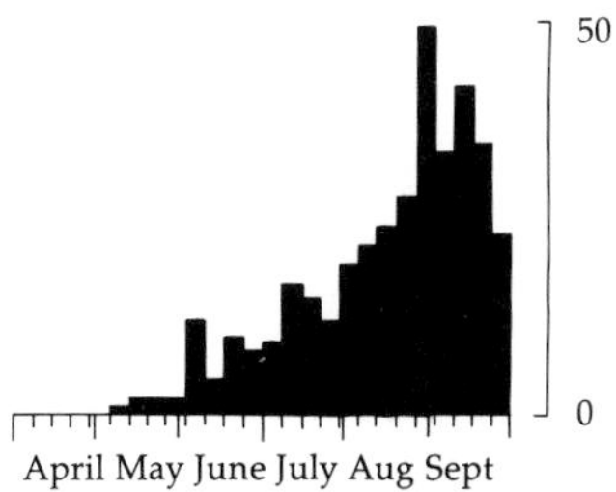

PAINTED LADY – *Cynthia cardui* Plate 39

The Painted Lady was considered to be both a migrant and resident in Purbeck by some Dorset entomologists, including Parkinson Curtis. Recent studies have shown that this is not the case. Few, if any, Painted Ladies survive the winter, even in the relatively mild climate of south Dorset. The populations seen each year are dependent on the large immigrations which occur annually from North Africa, southern Europe and other population centres. In most years, immigrants reach the Dorset coast in June, as shown by the first records on the histogram. Large migrations have been recorded elsewhere in Britain, also in late July and even in August. As a rule, the early migrants spread throughout the County. They may be seen laying eggs, almost obsessively, on thistle leaves (*Carduus* spp. and *Cirsium* spp.) and occasionally on other plants such as Mallows and Nettles. The larvae feed on the leaves and, after pupation, produce a larger generation of adults in the late summer. These may be seen in all habitats and often visit garden flowers, but are commonest in open sandy areas such as along the coastline and on heaths, and on the chalk and limestone downlands.

Distribution and Status

Because it is so mobile, the Painted Lady may be seen anywhere in Dorset and the map is obviously far from complete. Nevertheless, it demonstrates that most sightings are from the coast and other open habitats, which is not the case with our other common migrant, the Red Admiral. As with all migrants, numbers fluctuate greatly from year to year as the annual counts at Swanage and Studland show. In most years, numbers are lower than the Red Admiral but higher than the Clouded Yellow. An exception was the Clouded Yellow Year of 1983. Its status in the past does not seem to have been significantly different. E. H. C. noted that it occurred 'more or less commonly around Swanage every year', and Parkinson Curtis agreed. Haines, early this century, stated that it was 'never wholly absent from the Winfrith neighbourhood' and Bankes and Digby, refering to Purbeck in the late 19th century, wrote 'common in most seasons'. In the Blackmore Vale, Dale considered it to be 'very common in 1818 and 1879, and a few other seasons, scarce in others'. It is interesting to note that the years in which there have been large numbers of Painted Lady have not necessarily coincided with those in which there were large numbers of other species of migrant butterflies and moths.

Where to see: Anywhere, but especially on the coasts, heathlands and flowery downs.

When to see: Often in small numbers in June, then regularly in larger numbers in August, September, and occasionally October.

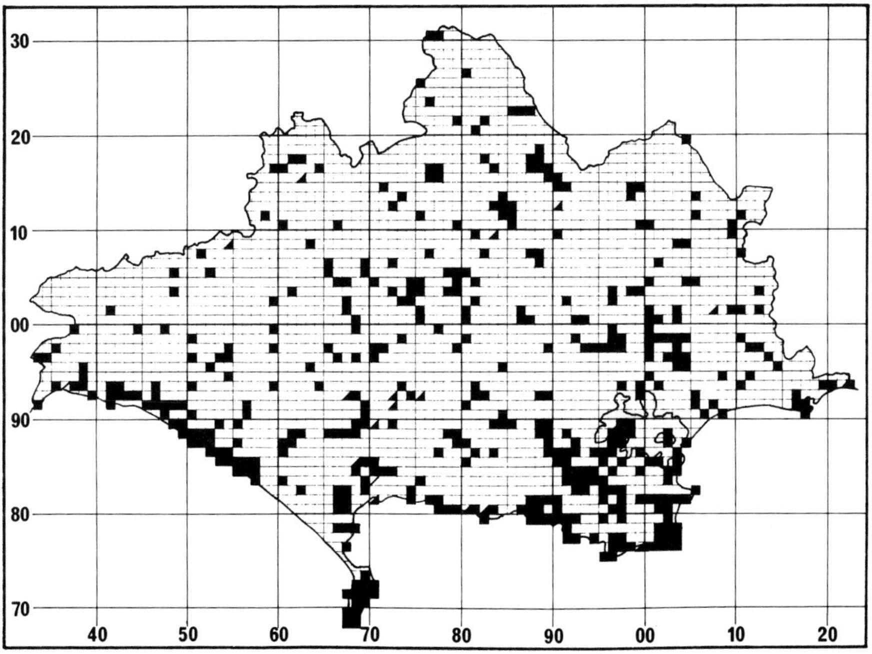

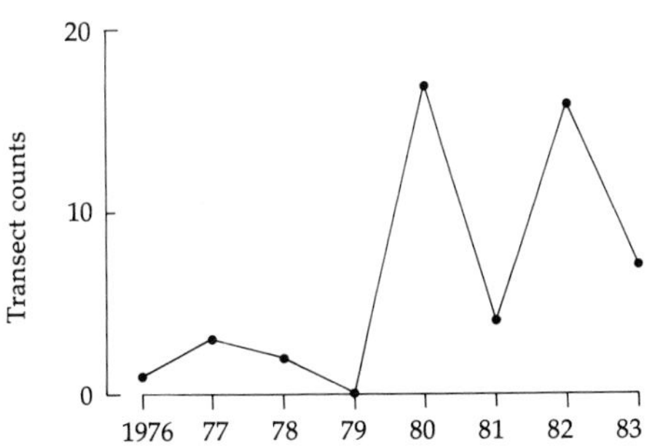

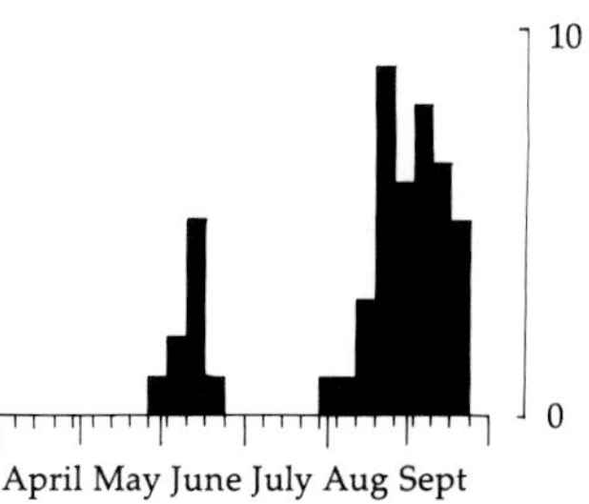

Fluctuations in Painted Lady numbers at Swanage and Studland.

SMALL TORTOISESHELL – *Aglais urticae* Plate 37

The Small Tortoiseshell perhaps the most familiar of all our butterflies and is the commonest member of the family Nymphalidae (Fritillaries, White Admiral, Peacock, etc.) in Dorset. It is a very mobile insect and is not confined to colonies. Instead it flies through town and country, feeding on flowers and breeding wherever it encounters suitable habitat. It has two broods a year; one in midsummer, the second in early autumn. The adults from the latter generation hibernate in buildings, outhouses, lofts, churches and even behind curtains. They are often seen fluttering in warm spells or when the heating is turned on. They reappear properly in the early spring and lay the eggs which produce the summer brood. Before hibernating, they gorge themselves on nectar and are seen in considerable numbers in gardens, where they feed on the late summer flowers. However, they seldom breed in gardens. The eggs are laid in large batches on Common and Annual Nettles (*Urtica dioica* and *U. urens*) and the caterpillars live gregariously in a web spun over the nettle leaves, until nearly full grown. Unlike the Peacock and Comma, which breed mainly in hedgerows and woodland edges, the Small Tortoiseshell also uses nettles growing in open fields, ditches, waste places and other open areas. There are many such suitable localities throughout the County.

Distribution and Status

The Small Tortoiseshell is a common butterfly that flies in all habitats throughout Dorset. We agree with Parkinson Curtis that 'it is indifferent to soil, elevation, or proximity to the sea'. The map reflects the distribution of recorders rather than that of the butterfly, and would be entirely black if recording had been complete (it should be noted that recorders seldom search for common species with the assidity that they seek rarities; consequently these latter species are better mapped). Although ubiquitous, the Small Tortoiseshell is probably seen in its greatest numbers in gardens. This gives a false impression of its abundance in the countryside as a whole. It seldom occurs in the huge numbers which are characteristic of many more local species. For example, it was exceeded by 15 other species (mainly Browns, Blues and Skippers) in the combined counts from Swanage, Studland and Fontmell between 1976 and 1984. It is also prone to considerable fluctuation from year to year, as shown by the annual counts. Both Dale and Parkinson Curtis considered that the Small Tortoiseshell was 'common' in Dorset, and there is no reason to believe that its status has changed in recent times.

Where to see: On garden flowers.

When to see: Adults come out of hibernation in the spring and can be seen on any warm day, mainly in late April and May. Subsequent generations vary in timing from year to year and are blurred in the combined counts. In general, there is an emergence in late June and early July and again in September. Adults fly well into October and can be found hibernating throughout the winter. Search for the larvae in late May and August.

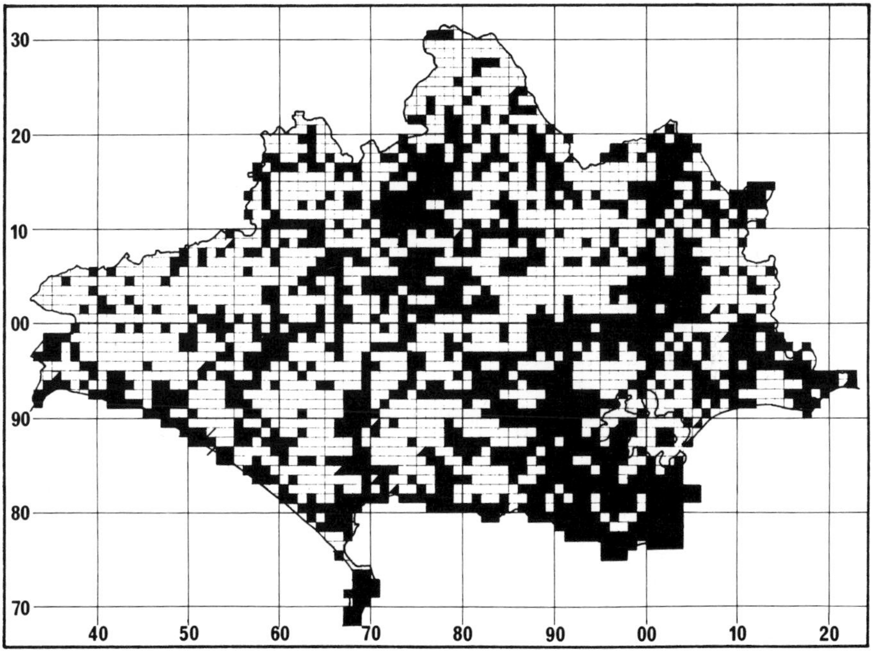

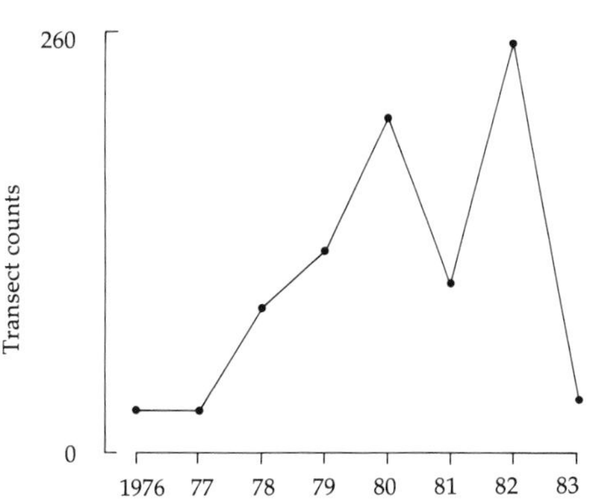

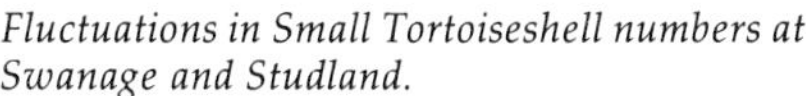

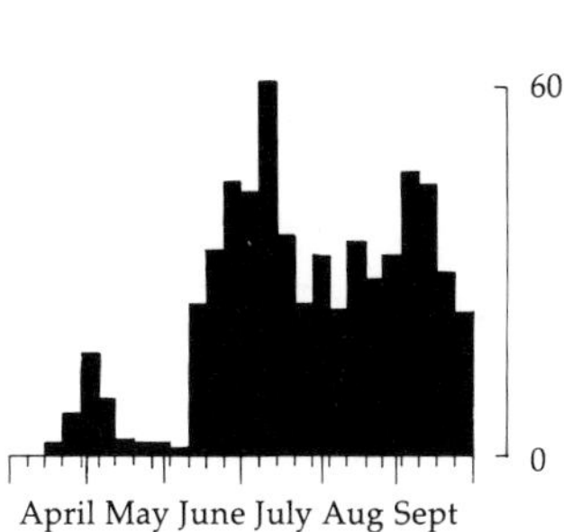

Fluctuations in Small Tortoiseshell numbers at Swanage and Studland.

PEACOCK – *Inachis io* Plate 40

This is a large and spectacular insect which is common and widespread throughout Dorset. Few people can fail to recognise its reddish brown upper wings edged with black, and blue peacock eyes, which contrast starkly with the dark, bark-like undersides. There is one brood a year, but adults are seen during two flight periods because they hibernate. Freshly emerged individuals gorge themselves for a few weeks in high summer on flowers, and then quite suddenly disappear, to re-emerge on sunny days in the following spring for a period of about six weeks. These butterflies hibernate in houses, churches, outhouses, lofts and hollow trees.

The Peacock does not live in strict colonies, but is a highly mobile butterfly, flying freely and breeding wherever suitable conditions occur. Although the majority of Dorset Peacocks are home bred, there is interchange with adjacent counties and, to a lesser extent, with the continent. The adults are seen in all habitats and are frequent visitors to garden flowers, especially Buddleia. However, the prefered habitat is woodland, and the greatest numbers are to be seen along woodland edges where Teasel (*Dipsacus fullonum*) and other nectar rich flowers grow. Breeding is generally in the vicinity of woodland or along sheltered hedgerows. Like other Vanessids, single males hold well spaced territories in places where the females fly. The eggs are laid on the undersides of the leaves of Nettles (*Urtica* spp.). The larvae live gregariously in a web, similar to that of the Small Tortoiseshell, spun over the leaves. The caterpillars of the Peacock are more uniformly black and grow larger than those of the Small Tortoiseshell.

Distribution and Status

Dale described the Peacock as 'generally distributed' in Dorset during the 19th century, whereas he described fifteen other species (including the Small Tortoiseshell, Brimstone and Large and Small Whites) as common. Haines, referring to the first quarter of this century, considered the Peacock to be 'common in the County', as did Parkinson Curtis, writing sixty years later, but with the qualification that it varied much in abundance. He added that 'nearly every year probably and in favourable years certainly there is no group of flowers whether in a town garden or a country hedgerow that will not be graced at a suitable time by this handsome insect and I am certain that every cloverfield in the month of August can be relied upon to produce some specimens. A list of localities would be meaningless as far as I can see'.

We have, nevertheless, included a map of all records received, which, if complete, would undoubtedly cover the whole County. In recent years, the Peacock has been common throughout Dorset and has not fluctuated noticeably in abundance. However, it is consistently more numerous in the wooded or well hedged and sheltered districts of the County, which are not necessarily the best recorded areas. Thus the Peacock is more numerous on the northern clays, and the central and northern chalk. Unlike Dale, we would rank the Peacock among the ten commonest Butterflies in Dorset, although the adults are seldom seen together in large numbers, as are some Browns and Blues. We consider that the Peacock has at least maintained its status in the County since the time of Dale.

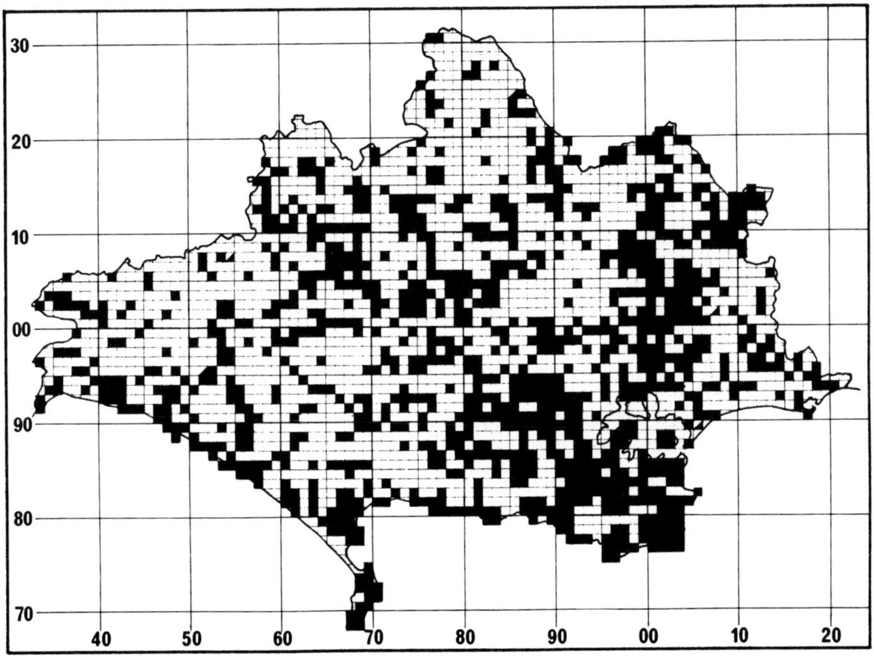

Where to see: Sunny flowery places; any wood; in gardens from August.

When to see: Sunny days in March, but mostly in April and May. Again in July and August.

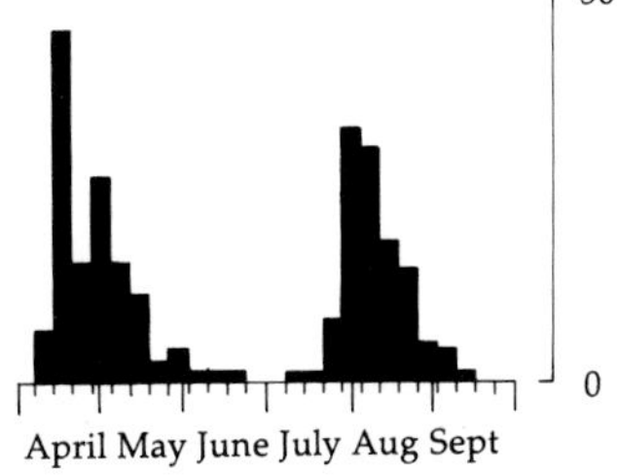

COMMA – *Polygonia c-album* Plates 35 and 36

During the past 150 years no butterfly in Dorset has experienced greater fluctuations in distribution and status than the Comma. From being widespread and locally common in the early 19th century, it declined and was more or less absent for 60 years. Then, this century, it gradually increased. Today, the Comma can be found wherever there are woods, copses or sheltered hedgerows.

Although the Comma not a migrant, it is a comparatively mobile butterfly. The adults may be seen visiting garden flowers to feed before hibernating, but they are more often seen at their breeding sites. These are the shrubby edges of sunny glades and rides in woods, woodland edges, and, to a lesser extent, hedgerows, especially those with adjacent trees or situated in sheltered hollows. The eggs are laid singly on the leaves of Nettles (*Urtica* spp.), Elms (*Ulmus* spp.) and Hop (*Humulus lupulus*). These plants have always been common in the hedges and woods of Dorset, and there is no evidence to suggest that the fluctuations in abundance of the last 150 years are linked to changes in the management of hedges and woods. However, nor have they been related to any other factor. Similar simultaneous fluctuations also occurred in most other counties.

Distribution and Status

Dale, writing in 1885, described the Comma as having been 'formerly in plenty at Glanvilles Wootton but none have been taken since 1816', whilst Bankes, in 1902, wrote 'formerly common locally, now almost extinct'. Despite Dale's early date for its disappearance in central Dorset, the Comma evidently persisted longer elsewhere. Parkinson Curtis, quotes Blanchard as saying that it was frequent enough in Dorset in his younger days (perhaps up to 1840) to call for no comment. The decline was then rapid and almost complete. There are two records of single adults during the second half of the 19th century, from Stinsford in 1887 and Portland in 1898. The next sightings were 'about the beginning of the 1910-20 decade, with reports of its presence on the north-west borders . . . by 1918 it had reached the Wareham district in fair numbers and it reached Parkstone in 1921.' Parkinson Curtis continues, 'By 1929 so very generally was it spread that a list of localities seems a little otiose . . . it was a feature of the autumnal landscape, and seemed to be everywhere in the County. Every blackberry bush had specimens feeding on the fruit and every garden had its Michaelmas Daisies decked with this attractive insect'. But he ended on a gloomy note, 'I fear that we shall have another half century of dearth. 1940 was distinctly a poor year though 1941 was better . . . by 1962 the recession had become very marked indeed but in 1964 H. J. Moore considers it was recovering a little'.

The Comma did indeed recover, as is evident from the map, which we consider to be far from complete. Most records were made from 1978 to 1984, and showed good numbers in most woods or wooded regions. Its present status is well short of Parkinson Curtis' description for 1929, but fits Blanchard's account for the early 19th century fairly well. Today, it is commonest in the wooded districts on the clays and chalk in the northern half of Dorset. Glanvilles Wootton, where Dale failed to see it for sixty years, is a very good area. Although there has been no sign of a decline during the last 20 years – indeed it has increased – there is no certainty that it will not, one day, mysteriously disappear again.

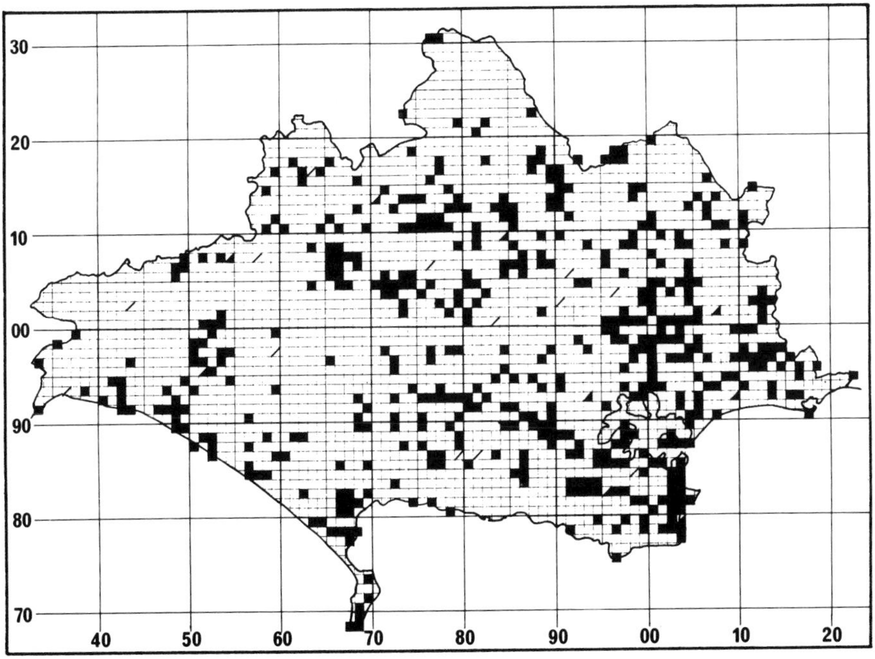

Where to see: Any sunny wood, especially large woods in the Blackmore Vale and on the central and northern chalk.

When to see: Hibernating adults emerge in the spring and are most often seen in April. There is a summer brood in late July, followed by another emergence in September. These adults feed well into October, after our recording period.

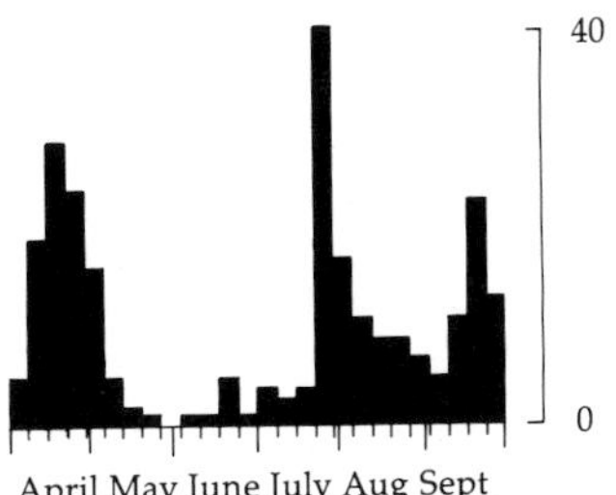

SMALL PEARL-BORDERED FRITILLARY *Boloria selene*

Plates 41 and 42

This small, dark and brightly coloured Fritillary was once a common sight in Dorset woods. Since the 1950s it has declined alarmingly and it must now be considered a rarity in the County. Unless the decline abates, we expect it to become extinct in Dorset within the next two decades, probably preceeded by the loss of the High Brown and Pearl-bordered Fritillaries.

In Dorset the main foodplant of the caterpillar is the Common Dog Violet (*Viola riviniana*). This butterfly breeds in distinct colonies, which may shift position from year to year but which seldom colonise new habitats in distant woods. Typical colonies are quite small, occupying less than an acre. They usually consist of tens of individuals, but may become extremely large in a season or two under ideal conditions. Little is known of the exact requirements of the different woodland Fritillaries. All are characteristic of sunny open woodlands, and all were locally common when coppicing was a wide-spread practice. Generally, the Small Pearl-bordered Fritillary prefers wetter soils and grassier clearings than the other species. It breeds in damp clearings, snipe bogs and rides, although not necessarily in freshly cut woodland blocks. Some colonies breed in rough grassland at the edges of woods, grassy heath and scrubby places, particularly in the west of the County where overgrown cliffs near woods may also be used. Everywhere it needs regular clearings or fires to cause a flush of young violets. This is now an uncommon form of land management in Dorset and has led to the decline of this species.

Distribution and Status

Dale described the Small Pearl-bordered Fritillary, without qualification, as 'common in woods'. Haines added that it was also 'locally common on rough heathy fields, downs and bushy places'. Parkinson Curtis, reviewing this century up to about 1950, considered it to be of a similar status to the Pearl-bordered Fritillary; that is, very common and sometimes abundant in woods in the County as a whole, and being the commoner of the two species in the wetter west, especially around Powerstock, Drakenorth and Hooke Park, but 'not at all common in the south-east of the County'. He added that, unlike its larger relative, the Small Pearl-bordered Fritillary was also found in heathy places.

Few old entomologists listed localities, and the map greatly under represents both its former distribution and the extent of the decline. Moreover, many recently recorded colonies are now extinct. Small populations survive in several localities, including heathy scrub in Purbeck and Milborne Wood, young coppice at Bloxworth, young plantations and recent clearings at Bere Regis, clearings near Bulbarrow Hill, on Cranborne Chase near Verwood, in marshy clearings in the Blackmoor Vale woods, amongst scrub at Lydlinch, and in woodlands in the west, such as Powerstock. About 30-40 fairly small colonies are estimated to survive, three to four times the number of the Pearl-bordered Fritillary, but many will become extinct in the near future.

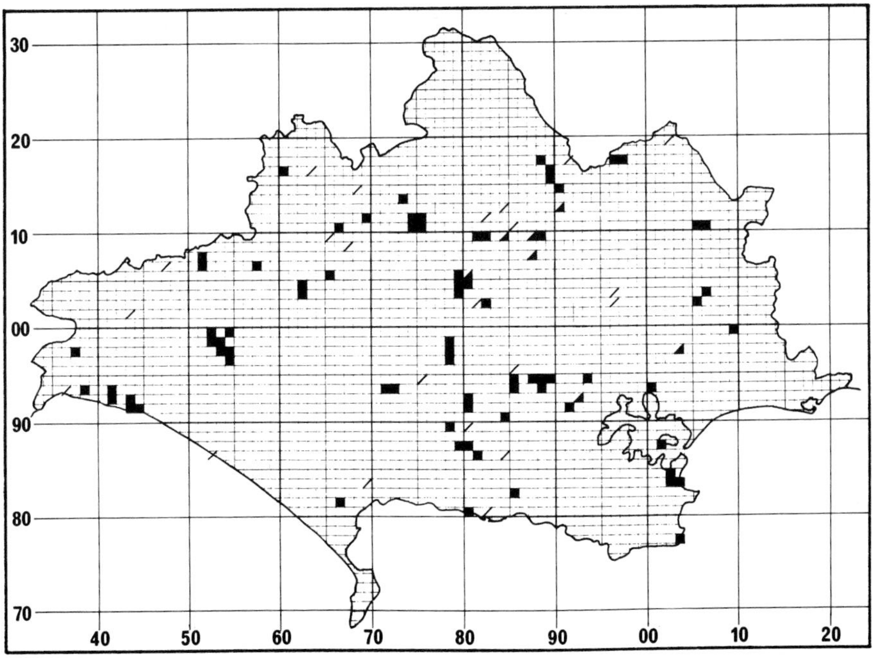

Where to see: Woodland rides around Powerstock; Lydlinch Common; public foot-paths in Milborne Wood; Bloxworth,

When to see: Poorly recorded on the transects, but generally seen in June and early July. An occasional second emergence in late summer.

PEARL-BORDERED FRITILLARY – *Boloria euphrosyne*

Plates 43 and 44

This insect emerges in May, two to three weeks earlier than the similar Small Pearl-bordered Fritillary. However there is some overlap and, until recently, these two Fritillaries were a common sight flying together in many Dorset woods. Today it is one of our most rapidly declining butterflies, and is in some danger of extinction.

Unlike its smaller relative, the Pearl-bordered Fritillary is strictly a woodland species in Dorset. The adults are seen flitting rapidly over the ground in sunny rides and glades, and over freshly cleared plots with a rich ground flora of Bugle, Primrose and other flowers. The eggs are laid on young Violets, especially the Common Dog Violet (*Viola riviniana*) growing in sunny, open, yet sheltered pockets. The caterpillars feed on the leaves and bask openly on the warm ground.

Colonies of this Fritillary can exist in quite small woodland clearings, often of less than a hectare. Ideal breeding conditions were continually created when woods were regularly coppiced, with the butterfly circulating to the new areas as the old became shaded. With the abandonment of coppicing, many colonies became extinct as entire woods became shadier. The cessation of rabbit grazing in the 1950s may also have been a contributory factor. Other populations briefly flourished as woods were cleared for conifer plantations, but these too ultimately became extinct. Today, the few colonies that survive fly in fragments of woodland in which the coppice cycle is maintained and on one or two other sites. However, they are becoming so isolated that any new suitable habitat is unlikely to be colonised, since the butterfly is not very mobile.

Distribution and Status

In Victorian times and during the first quarter of this century, the Pearl-bordered Fritillary was described, without further comment by Dale as 'common in woods' and by Haines as 'a common woodland butterfly'. It was too widespread for localities to be worth listing, hence the map is a gross underrepresentation of the past distribution. Parkinson Curtis, writing in the 1950s, agreed with Dale and Haines about its status, but added: 'except as to the heath areas. In the small woods of the heath areas it is either absent or scarce, in the large woods it is common. In the north and west of the County it is abundant'. He also wrote that he had seen many thousands of Dorset specimens.

Local extinctions started in the late 1950s and colonies became very scarce in 1970s; no butterfly in the County has declined more rapidly in recent years. Scores of woods, on all soils, were searched in 1983-84, but only two new colonies were discovered, near to recent records. At the time of writing, probably fewer than fifteen relict populations exist, scattered throughout the County at Powerstock, Bracketts' Coppice, in fresh coppice near Bloxworth, in several clearings on Cranborne Chase and perhaps elsewhere. Most of the other recent records on the map are already extinct, and the future of the surviving colonies is bleak.

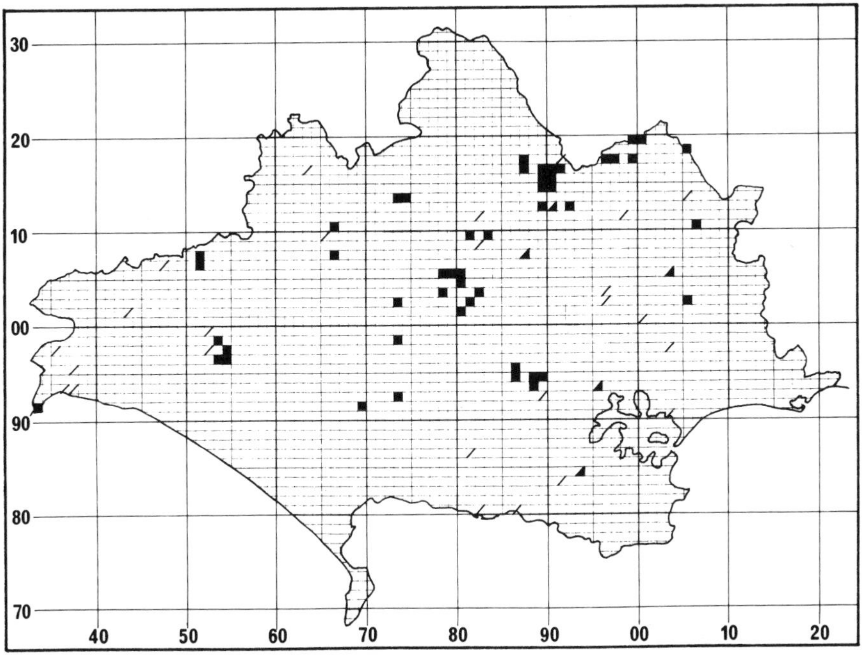

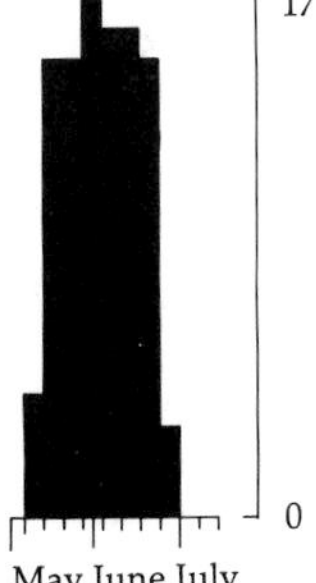

Where to see: Public footpaths at Powerstock and Stubhampton Bottom.

When to see: Late May and early June.

HIGH BROWN FRITILLARY – *Argynnis adippe* Plate 45

Up to 30 years ago this beautiful Fritillary could be found in many of the large deciduous woods in the County. Today, it is on the verge of extinction and is probably confined to one location where it was last reliably seen in 1982. We doubt if it will survive here for long. East of Dorset, it has already disappeared from at least ten counties, in some of which it was the commonest Fritillary only 30 years ago. It has fared better to the west, and although declining, good colonies survive locally in Devon, Wales and the Lake District.

This is a butterfly of large extensive woodlands. Like the other common Fritillaries, the caterpillars feed on the leaves of Violets (*Viola* spp.). Little is known of its exact requirements but when egglaying it seems to prefer violets growing in more open and sunnier areas within woods than the three other woodland Fritillaries. It probably also needs larger areas of suitable habitat for survival. Favourite places are compartments of young coppice, rough grass, or scattered shrubs within large woods, especially if the ground flora is sparse, as often occurs after a fire, or when grazed by deer or rabbits. There is little doubt that the decline of the High Brown Fritillary has been caused by the abandonment of coppicing and the increased shadiness of both broadleaved and coniferous woodlands. The loss of rabbits in the mid 1950s may have been an exacerbating factor, causing the ground flora to become too overgrown.

It is still worth looking for this butterfly in the larger woods in the County, since recording has not been comprehensive. However, naturalists who are unfamiliar with the species should be aware of two common mistakes. The name High Brown should not be taken literally. A brown Fritillary flying high over the canopy of a Dorset wood is almost certainly a female Silver-washed Fritillary, possibly the dark *valezina* form. Secondly, the Dark Green Fritillary, which is very similar in appearance, breeds at low densities in a few woods, although its usual habitat is open grassland. Today there are many more Dark Green than High Brown Fritillaries flying in Dorset woods.

Distribution and Status

In 1886 Dale failed to comment on the status of the High Brown Fritillary but Bankes, in the same decade, considered it to be 'widely distributed and sometimes locally common' in Dorset. Seventy years later Parkinson Curtis thought that Bankes' assessment was still, 'a fair summary of the status of the species', although it was 'apparently rare in Purbeck'. He noted that it had increased greatly during the period from 1914 to 1918, which he attributed to the reduction in gamekeeping and pheasant rearing, which led to a better survival of the larvae. More significantly, he stated, 'but now in 1958 the retrogression seems to have been acute.' The butterfly has been in decline ever since. Of the few recent sightings, most have been from a string of woodlands on the chalk hills from Delcombe Wood near Hilton, extending north-eastwards into the woods of Cranborne Chase. It has been impossible to verify all recent records but it should be noted that the Silver-washed Fritillary occurs in all these woods and the Dark Green Fritillary on much of the neighbouring downland. Several records are definite and they include what we believe to be the only surviving colony in Dorset.

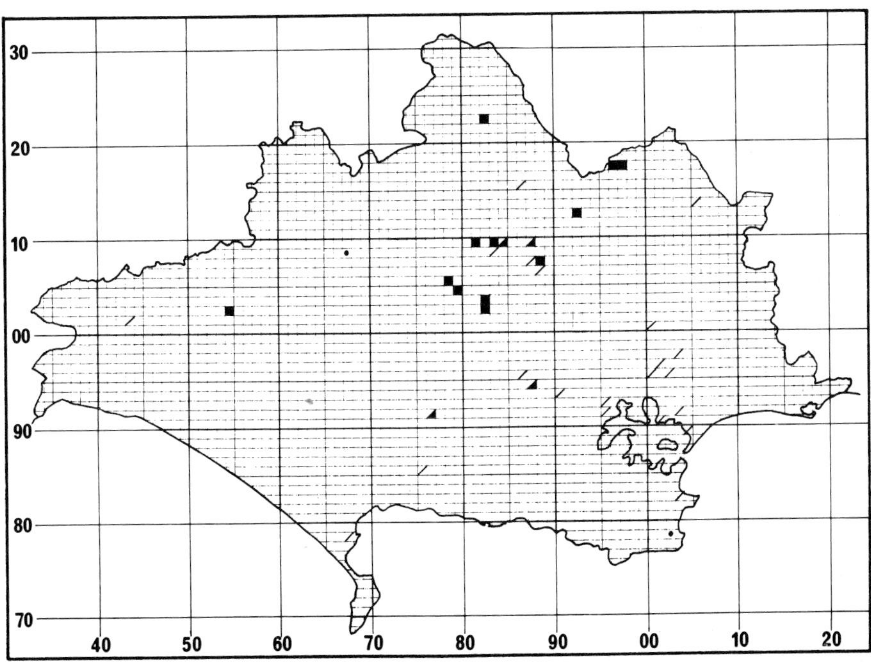

<table>
<tr><td>Where to see:</td><td>No longer in Dorset; in woods on the fringes of Dartmoor, Devon.</td></tr>
<tr><td>When to see:</td><td>Late June and early July.</td></tr>
</table>

DARK GREEN FRITILLARY – *Argynnis aglaja* Plate 46

This Fritillary breeds mainly in rough open grassland, and is still a familiar sight in midsummer along much of the coastline and on certain flowery downs. It is usually seen in ones and twos, and is a very striking butterfly. It dwarfs the more numerous Meadow Browns, Marbled Whites, Skippers and Blues, and whilst these butterflies flutter from flower to flower, it glides majestically over the hillside, pausing to feed on thistles,

The eggs of this Fritillary are laid singly on or near to clumps of violets, generally in open grassland. The larva enters hiberation immediately after hatching and does not feed on the violet leaves until the spring. Several species of violet are eaten, but the the Hairy Violet (*Viola hirta*) is a favourite and is probably the most commonly used food plant in Dorset.

Although it is a powerful flyer, the Dark Green Fritillary restricts itself to more or less discrete colonies and is unlikely to be seen far from its breeding sites. These are where violets grow in local abundance as large bushy plants in a warm, fairly open sward, that is from 5 to 10 cm tall. Unfortunately, suitable sites are becoming much rarer on the chalk and limestone hills because of agricultural improvements. The habitat of the Dark Green Fritillary has survived rather better along the cliffs and undercliffs, where erosion and landslips create a succession of vegetation. Small colonies of this butterfly breed in woodland, especially on the chalk, using the extensive areas of rough grass which may occur in short-cycled coppice plots or in rides. Few people associate this butterfly with woodland, and it is very often misidentified as the High Brown Fritillary, once common in Dorset woods, but today all but extinct.

Distribution and Status

In the 19th century, Dale described this Fritillary as, 'generally distributed but not common' and perhaps this reflects the fact that most sheepwalks, although unimproved, were too heavily stocked for large colonies to develop. In the present century, Parkinson Curtis, considered this species to be locally common, 'both as to distribution and numbers of individuals, easily the commonest of our large Fritillaries'. Today, that accolade almost certainly belongs to the Silver-washed Fritillary. The main sites for the Dark Green Fritillary now lie in south-east Dorset and on the north-east chalk. In Purbeck, it still may be seen almost anywhere along the chalk hills and the limestone coast but usually nowadays as single individuals. Large numbers breed on the chalk around Lulworth and westwards to Portland but on the coast in the west of the County it is again scarce, although well distributed. We believe it has been poorly recorded both in this area and inland. Small woodland colonies breed around Powerstock and scattered colonies have recently occurred along the steep chalk hills between Piddletrenthide and Shaftesbury. Reasonable colonies survive around Fontmell, and in the far north-east there are still good colonies on Martin Down. Many chalk colonies are believed to be extinct and numbers have been declining everywhere over the last decade. Although not yet a rarity, this species has become a scarce insect in most of the County, even on the coast.

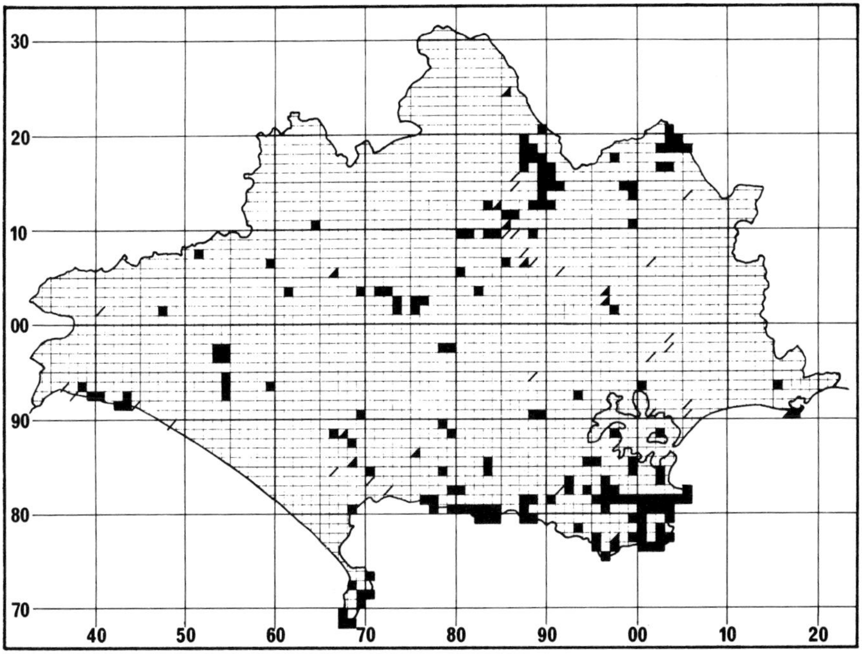

30
20
10
00
90
80
70
40
50
60
70
80
90
00
10
20

Where to see: Martin Down, Portland and Purbeck Coast.

When to see: Mid June to early August.

40
0
June July Aug Sept

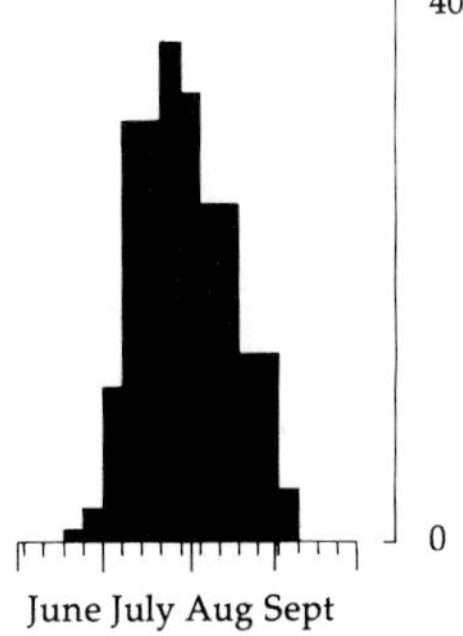

SILVER-WASHED FRITILLARY – *Argynnis paphia* Plate 48

Of the five Fritillaries that were once common in Dorset, only the Silver-washed remains in any numbers. The male is a very large, golden butterfly with distinctive streaks on the upperwings; the female is darker and lacks the streaks. There is a dusky green form of the female, named *valezina*, which is rare in most years, but in hot summers, it may constitute about one in 10 to 15 of the female population. Contrary to popular belief, we have found *valezina* females to be equally common in all parts of the County. Females of this form are often mistaken for other species, especially the Dark Green Fritillary.

In Dorset, the Silver-washed Fritillary is a woodland butterfly. It is a strong flyer and sometimes individuals may be seen in woodlands where there is no permanent colony. It is on the wing in July and August, soaring among the tree tops or floating down to a sunny patch of flowering brambles in a ride or clearing. The eggs are laid singly in chinks in the bark of trees, 3 to 4 feet up on the north, mossy side of the trunks, and always in localities where violets (usually *Viola riviniana*) grow abundantly in the ground flora. The newly-hatched caterpillar immediately hibernates in the bark and descends in the following spring to feed on the violets. It is partial to the lobes of the leaves, and its characteristic bites are quite easily found in May.

The Silver-washed Fritillary breeds in shadier places than other common woodland Fritillaries, which probably explains why, so far, it has survived much better in Dorset, despite the increasing shadiness of modern woods. Areas where dappled light penetrates to the ground are preferred, especially where violets are abundant. Broadleaved woodlands with standards which exclude about 50 per cent of the sunlight are ideal, but like abandoned coppices, continue to support small numbers for many years as the canopy becomes more closed. Dense conifer plantations become unsuitable very quickly, but may support small colonies where there are clearings.

Distribution and Status

In the 19th century, both Dale and Haines described the Silver-washed Fritillary as being common in woodland districts of Dorset, whilst Bankes considered it to be 'occasionally common'. Parkinson Curtis, earlier this century, agreed with Bankes and noted that it was only abundant in occasional years, when it wandered over wide areas.

Today this butterfly is still very well distributed throughout Dorset, although many locations on the map probably refer to strays and not to colonies. Nonetheless, one can expect to see a few adults in any year in all the larger woods in the County, regardless of soil type, with the exception of large mature plantations such as most of Wareham Forest. Fine colonies exist on the chalk on Cranborne Chase, around Crichel and to the east of Dorchester. Large numbers also breed in all the Blackmoor Vale woods, Middlemarsh and in the west, for example at Powerstock. In warm years adults are abundant in all these woods and reasonably common elsewhere. However, the overall trend in numbers seems to be downwards, and we would expect this butterfly to become considerably scarcer in Dorset as many of the woodlands mature.

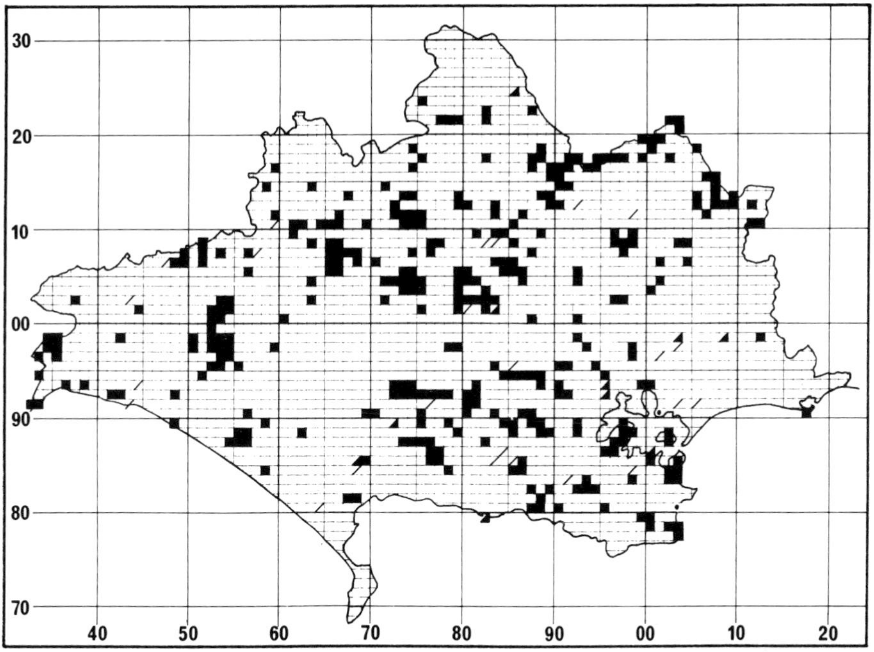

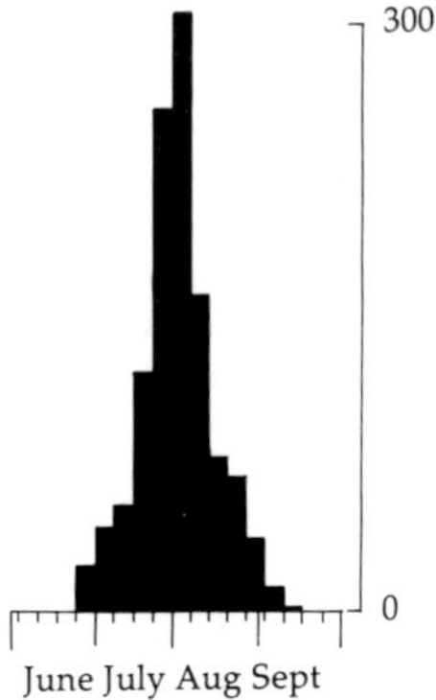

Where to see: In clearings and rides, especially in open broad-leaved woods throughout the County.

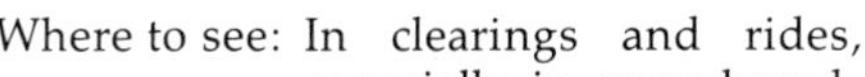

When to see: Adults in July and August.

MARSH FRITILLARY – *Eurodryas aurinia* Plate 47

The Marsh Fritillary is one of Europe's most rapidly declining butterflies. It is already extinct in the Netherlands and in many of the counties of eastern England but it remains locally common in Wales and in the west of England. Dorset lies between these extremes, and although most colonies have been lost, some fine ones survive. The decline has been more severe than the map suggests because recording was patchy in the past and some colonies were not defined precisely enough for inclusion on the map, whereas recent surveys have been very detailed. In addition, several of the records since 1969 have been of strays.

These beautiful butterflies are found in self-contained colonies, but sometimes individuals will stray for several kilometres, especially in hot summers. Most breeding sites are small and consist of flowery, unfertilised grassland where the larval foodplant, Devil's-bit Scabious (*Succisa pratensis*) is common. Occasional light mowing or grazing is essential otherwise the scabious becomes unsuitable for egg laying, and is itself eventually shaded out of the sward. Most fields where the foodplant grows are too heavily grazed for this Fritillary, and Parkinson Curtis noticed a great increase in numbers during the First World War, when farming was less intense, and a decline afterwards when stocking rates increased. Ideal sites have a patchy turf from 5 to 15 centimetres in height. The eggs are laid in batches of up to 300, but only on quite large, prominent scabious plants.

In Dorset, Devil's-bit Scabious grows in two contrasting habitats; in damp meadows on heavy soils and on dry chalk downland. Colonies of the Marsh Fritillary breed in both situations, although those on the chalk are a recent phenomenon. In the 19th century colonies were found, very locally, only in the marshy meadows that give this butterfly its name. Today, these flower-rich meadows have virtually disappeared through agricultural improvements and drainage, and the remaining colonies in this habitat breed on common land and grassland associated with woods. However, on the downland, most of the rare patches which have not been improved are now only lightly grazed, favouring the growth of large Scabiouses that are suitable for the butterfly. The first known downland colony was on Hod Hill, which established itself some time between 1905 and 1920 and which still survives. More recently, eight other colonies have been found and now outnumber traditional marshland sites. However, this limited spread on downland by no means compensates for the losses elsewhere.

Distribution and Status

Colonies are less well distributed than the map suggests, due to strays and recent extinctions. Of the marshland sites, the large colony at Verwood was lost in 1981 through building developments. A famous colony survives in common land at Lydlinch, though diminishing in numbers as the site becomes overgrown. Much larger colonies exist nearby in woodland clearings, rough fields and young plantations in the Blackmoor Vale. There are two medium-sized colonies in the west on DNT reserves at Powerstock and Brackett's Coppice. The chalk colonies are mainly small, at Martin Down, Bottlebrush Down near Fontmell, Hod Hill, possibly Cheselbourne and on steep hills near Cerne Abbas. Four colonies (two marshland and two chalk) in Dorset breed on nature reserves and these alone seem likely to survive in the future.

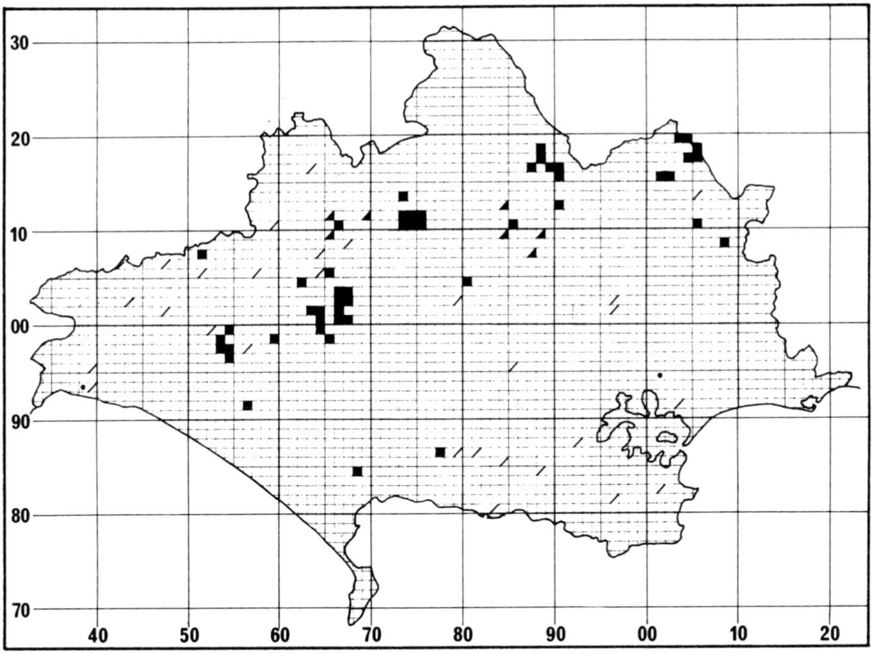

Where to see: Hod Hill, Lydlinch Common.

When to see: Adults from mid May to mid June. Nests of young black larvae basking on silk webs spun around Devil's-bit Scabious in July and March. By April smaller clusters, then single larvae are conspicuous.

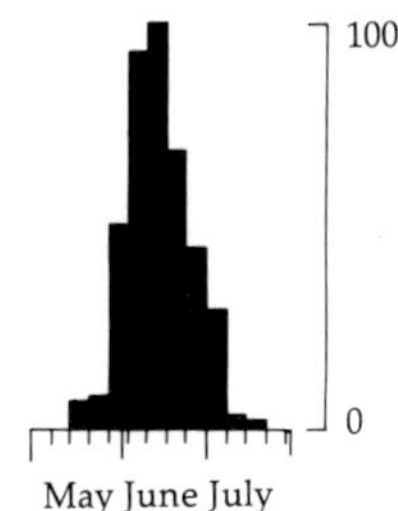

SPECKLED WOOD – *Pararge aegeria* Plate 52

The Speckled Wood may be seen from April until October almost everywhere in the County where there are trees, tall hedgerows or scrub. It is one of the more heartening sights of the modern countryside of Dorset for, in the first half of this century, it was much rarer.

Like all Browns, the larvae feed on wild grasses, of which Cocksfoot (*Dactylis glomerata*) and Common Couch (*Agropyron repens*) are considered to be the favourites. Eggs are laid on only those plants growing in shade, which restricts breeding to the ground flora beneath woods, hedges and scrub. This butterfly seldom strays from its breeding sites and a colony can be supported by a very small area of suitable habitat. By far its favourite habitat is woodland and the Speckled Wood can tolerate – indeed prefers – much shadier conditions than most other species. The largest numbers are to be found in neglected coppices, copses or maturing broadleaved woodland, where dappled light just penetrates to the ground and where rides and glades are in semi-shade. The males are to be found perched on a leaf or indulging in a dancing flight in sunny spots in the wood. Both sexes spend long periods on the canopies of trees drinking aphid honeydew. Because it can tolerate shade, the Speckled Wood is also common in many middle-aged conifer plantations and is usually the last species to be shaded out as these mature into dense oppressive plots. Despite its fondness for shade, the Speckled Wood also breeds in many hedgerows, especially in the west of the County, and may also be common on some cliffs and undercliffs.

Distribution and Status

Up to the 1880s, Victorian naturalists considered the Speckled Wood to be a common and widespread butterfly in Dorset but then a severe decline began (as it did throughout Britain) and the species disappeared from most areas. For example, Hod Hill, Parkinson Curtis wrote 'not seen here between 1895 and 1925; taken in 1925, steady increase since'. and he qualifies a record by Haines for Bloxworth with; 'but it must be very scarce there as I have not seen it and I was there a great deal from 1895 to 1920'. It is worth quoting Parkinson Curtis fully on this species. Triggered by Dale's dismissive summary that in Dorset it was 'common', he wrote in about 1950, 'It was at one time strictly localised and until recently I personally had never seen it on any geological horizon younger than the Reading Beds. It has since 1908 shown a distinct tendency to increase particularly in the shady lanes of west Dorset and since 1938 has spread into the eastern part of the County in some numbers but there is a marked recession since 1948. L. Tatchell . . . considers it common throughout Purbeck.'

The detailed records support Parkinson Curtis' statement of a gradual increase through most of this century but his recession of 1948 was short lived. Today, the Speckled Wood is very well distributed and common on all soils throughout Dorset, and the map is by no means complete. The decline and recovery are difficult to explain satisfactorily. The area of habitat available to this species has increased greatly throughout this century as woods have become more shady and new plantations established. In addition, the increase in tall grasses since the loss of rabbits has probably been beneficial. But these facts do not explain why this butterfly was common in Victorian times, when woods were coppiced, and why it declined so suddenly.

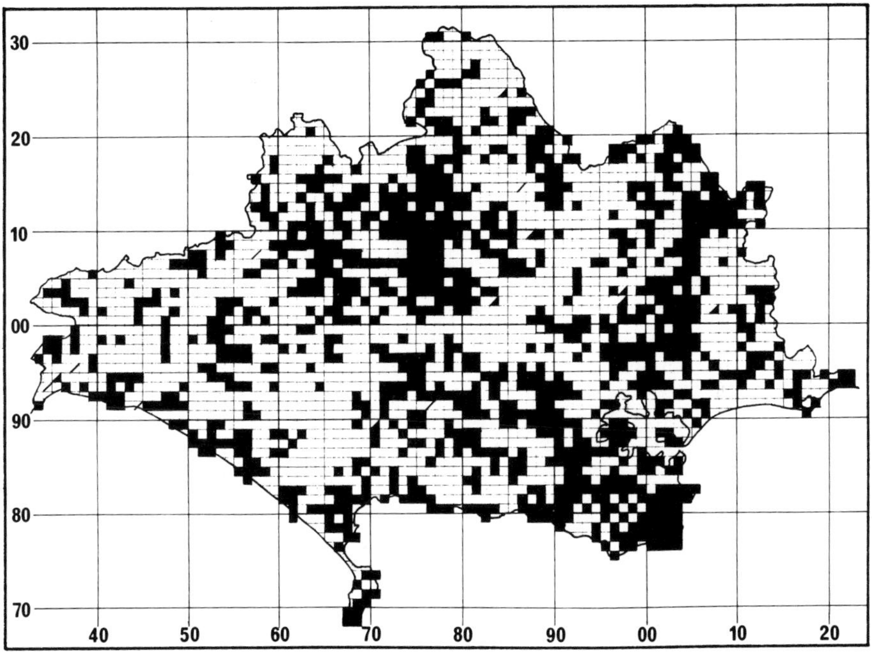

Where to see: Any somewhat shady wood, especially along rides; scrub on cliffs; overgrown hedges.

When to see: Any time between April and October. However there are distinct peaks which get larger through the year. The first in the early spring consists of butterflies which overwintered as pupae; the second in June is from butterflies which overwintered as larvae. These produce one or possible two further broods, peaking in early September and continuing until October.

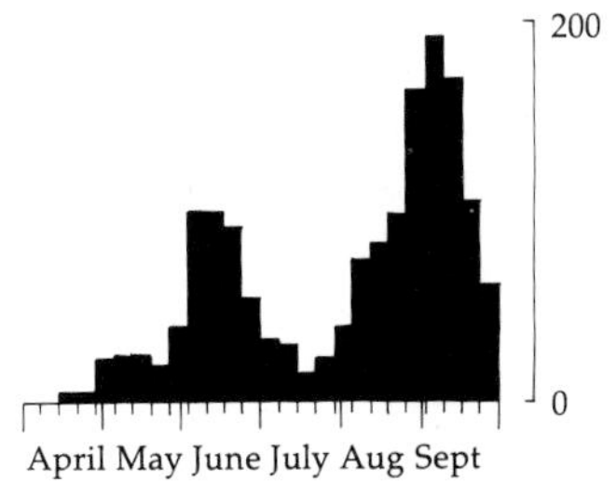

WALL – *Lasiommata megera* Plate 53

The Wall can be found in a wide variety of habitats throughout Dorset in late spring and again in late summer. In warm years, there may even be a third brood in the autumn. The Wall is seldom seen in large numbers; two or three individuals flying among tens of Ringlets or hundreds of Gatekeepers and Meadow Browns is usual. The wings are much more orange and brighter than the other Browns, and an adult glimpsed briefly is often mistaken for a Comma or even a Fritillary. However, when resting, the Wall can be identified by its eyespots.

The caterpillars feed mainly on Tor Grass (*Brachypodium pinnatum*) and False Brome (*B. sylvaticum*) but also on Cocksfoot (*Dactylis glomerata*), Yorkshire Fog (*Holcus lanatus*) and Wavy-hair Grass (*Deschampsia flexuosa*). Places where these grasses grow in uniform or dense swards are avoided. Instead, the eggs are laid in recently disturbed patches where the vegetation is sparse, such as hoofprints, rabbit scrapes, the bare edges of paths and sheep walks, and crumbly chalk scree. Breeding is concentrated into a few local spots and a very small area or strip of land can support a colony, making the eggs easy to find. In woodlands and hedgerows the eggs are laid on sheltered grasses growing in sunny spots.

The commonest sites for the Wall are steep thin-soiled banks on unimproved downs; abandoned clay, sand, lime and chalk pits; undercliffs; and rough recently disturbed wasteland. Smaller numbers may be seen along almost any hedgebank and along rides in open woods. Colonies rarely occur in lush meadows, bogs, heathlands and gardens. Together with its food plants, the butterfly is absent from leys, improved meadows and arable land.

Distribution and Status

Dale said that the Wall was common in Dorset in the 19th century, whereas Haines considered it to be 'fairly common and well distributed, but decreasing.' Towards the end of the last century Parkinson Curtis agreed with Haines, but thought it had increased since then and 'in 1943 was as abundant as it was when I started collecting.' He adds 'there is probably not a parish in the County that cannot produce scores of places to its liking.' This is still true today, although there are undoubtedly far fewer sites than formerly, especially on farmland. It is virtually absent from improved fields, yet many of these sites must have supported colonies in the past. In addition, unfertilised downs, hedgebanks, rough grassland and undercliffs probably supported much higher numbers when these were regularly grazed. Woodland populations were almost certainly larger when coppicing was commonplace. Nevertheless, colonies are still very well distributed throughout Dorset and are probably under represented on the map compared with many butterflies, because the Wall is a species which is often overlooked on a brief visit to a site due to its small population size. At present, it is probably most numerous along the coast and on the chalk downs.

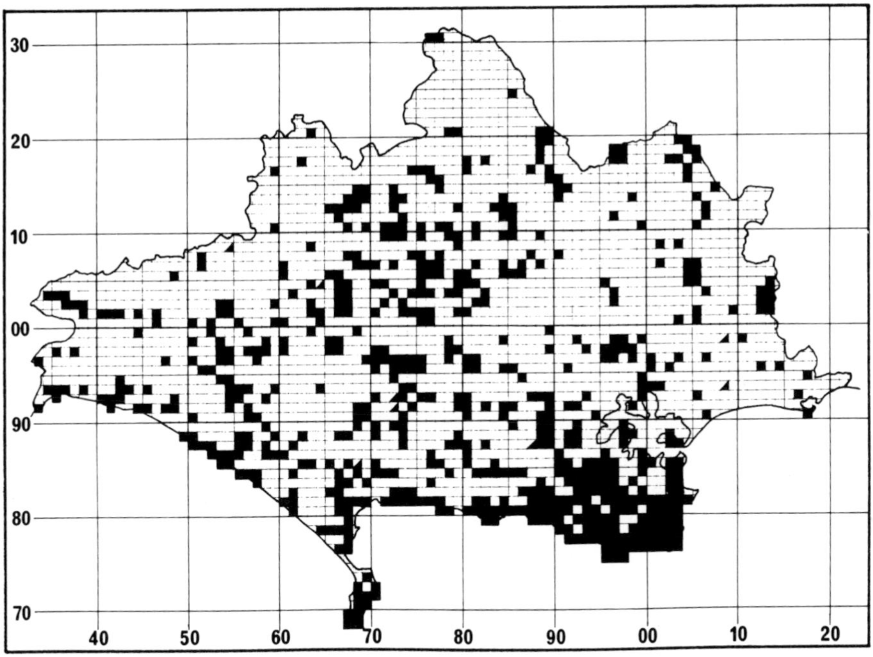

Where to see: Along footpaths on flowery downs; in warm sunny nooks on wasteland and undercliffs; abandoned quarries on all soils.

When to see: First generation adults in late May and early June. The second brood is invariable larger – usually twice the size – and peaks in late August. Small numbers are occasionally seen in October, too late for our recording period.

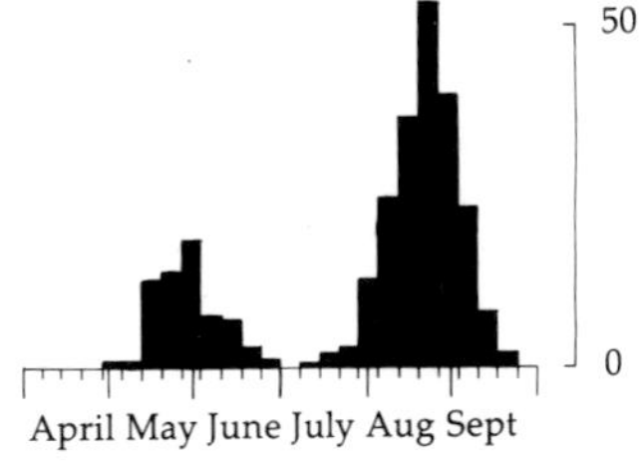

MARBLED WHITE – *Melanargia galathea* Plate 54

With its lazy flapping flight and distinctive black-and-white chequered wings, the Marbled White is one of the most attractive features of the Dorset countryside in high summer. It has a curious distribution in Britain, being widespread and locally common in south-western England but very local elsewhere. Fortunately, Dorset lies well within its range and this beautiful butterfly is a familiar sight feeding on knapweed, scabious and thistles on many unimproved grasslands.

As with all the Browns, the adults usually fly strictly within their compact breeding sites, although occasionally straying during hot dry weather to unlikely habitats, such as gardens. The eggs are dropped on to the grass and after hibernating when quite small, the larvae feed on Red Fescue (*Festuca rubra*), although there are reliable reports of Sheep's Fescue (*F. ovina*), Timothy (*Phleum pratense*), Cocksfoot (*Dactylis glomerata*) and Tor Grass (*Brachypodium pinnatum*) serving as food plants.

Marbled White colonies are commonest on calcareous grassland, especially where the sward is fairly tall and not dominated by coarse grasses. Heavy grazing or the improvement of grassland for agriculture ruins the habitat for the Marbled White. Many colonies persist in small pockets, along verges and tracks, and this accounts for those colonies found across the heathlands. Sunny, grassy rides in woods on the chalk invariably support a colony and several large populations breed in woods on the heavy clays and on the mixed soils of west Dorset. Small colonies consist of well under 100 individuals but much larger populations develop in extensive areas of wild grassland, especially in lightly grazed or abandoned downland and along the coast.

Distribution and Status

Dale considered the Marbled White to be common on chalk in the 19th century, but rare elsewhere, whereas Parkinson Curtis considered it to have been strictly local early this century. This is surprising but perhaps reflects the more intensive grazing that occurred on unimproved grassland in those days. It is difficult to say if it has increased overall since then. On the one hand, it has been eliminated from huge areas of farmland by the intensification of agricultural practices, on the other hand, the remaining fragments of grassland often grow tall and support large colonies of the Marbled White. Likewise, road verges have become over grown through diminished rabbit grazing, and a decrease in the frequency of cutting. In the future, the Marbled White will probably be eliminated from most farmland but should survive elsewhere on much other grassland.

At present, the Marbled White may be found throughout Dorset, especially on the chalk and limestone hills and everywhere along the coast where there is rough grassland. Small colonies breed on many road verges, even on the Tertiary soils and in most woods, including those in the Blackmoor Vale and in west Dorset.

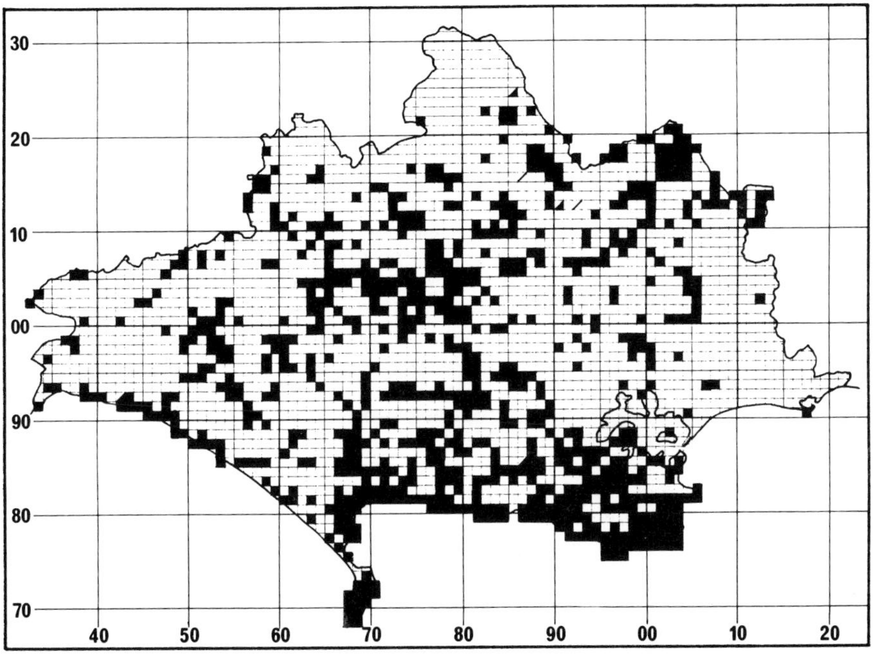

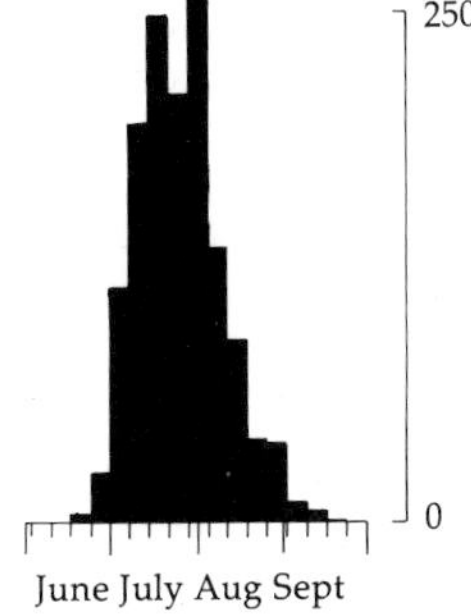

Where to see: Flowery, quite tall, chalk and limestone grasslands, especially along the coast.

When to see: July and August.

GRAYLING – *Hipparchia semele* Plate 56

The Grayling has declined alarmingly during the last 30 years at inland localities throughout the British Isles, and it is now rare except on the southern heathlands and along the coast: Dorset is one of its strongholds.

Known to Dale as the Black-eyed Marble, this attractive butterfly is the largest British Brown. The adult emerges in midsummer and has an idiosyncratic flight consisting of looping hops and short swift glides between nearby resting places. It alights on sunny patches of bare ground and after standing upright for a second or two with the wings closed, it then drops the forewings behind the hindwings, so that the conspicuous eye-spot is hidden. Finally, the butterfly leans into the sun so that it casts the minimum shadow. When in this posture the butterfly is extremely well camouflaged. The Grayling forms discrete colonies all over the heathlands and locally on dry calcareous grasslands, where it chooses very closely grazed vegetation or slopes that have a crumbly skeletal soil such as abandoned quarries. There are also many colonies along the coasts where erosion creates similar conditions. In the past, heavy grazing by sheep and rabbits on the downs caused damage and erosion to the turf, thus creating many suitable sites for this butterfly. This was also true to a lesser extent on some of the heavier soils. The eggs are laid in July and August, singly on the leaves of fine-leaved grasses. The larva feeds on a variety of grasses before hibernating and resuming feeding in the spring. It pupates in the soil in early June.

Distribution and Status

In the 19th century the Grayling occurred throughout Dorset and was ranked by Dale in his second commonest class of butterflies; those that were described without further comment as 'generally distributed'. Parkinson Curtis, writing in the early 1960s, added only a few qualifications. He considered it to be scarcest on the liassic clays and shales, but common everywhere, 'on open land that is not cultivated' or which '. . . has for long time gone out of cultivation'. It was also present on bogs but absent from 'lush marshy land'. He considered it to be abundant on the untouched heather and on uncultivated downs and stony uplands.

Today, the Grayling has practically disappeared from central and northern Dorset. The recent scattered records from the chalk between Dorchester, Shaftesbury and Martin Down refer to occasional sightings and most of these colonies are now extinct because their localities have become overgrown. Small chalkland colonies still exist along the southern face of the Purbeck Hills and in most abandoned quarries and cuttings and, the Grayling is still locally common along the limestone and chalk undercliffs of south-east Dorset and on the broken terrain of Portland. A few colonies exist on cliffs in the extreme west and inland on stony soil on grassy places associated with woods. By far the finest colonies breed on the heathlands, as is evident from the map. Although there have been losses here too, populations have survived well among all the plantations, breeding in young grassy plots, especially along the firebreaks. It is still the commonest Brown wherever heathland vegetation survives, and there is no evidence that it has declined on these extensive areas. Interesting isolated colonies exist further west in the County where there are pockets of heathland; the large colony on Black Down (Hardy's Monument) is a good example.

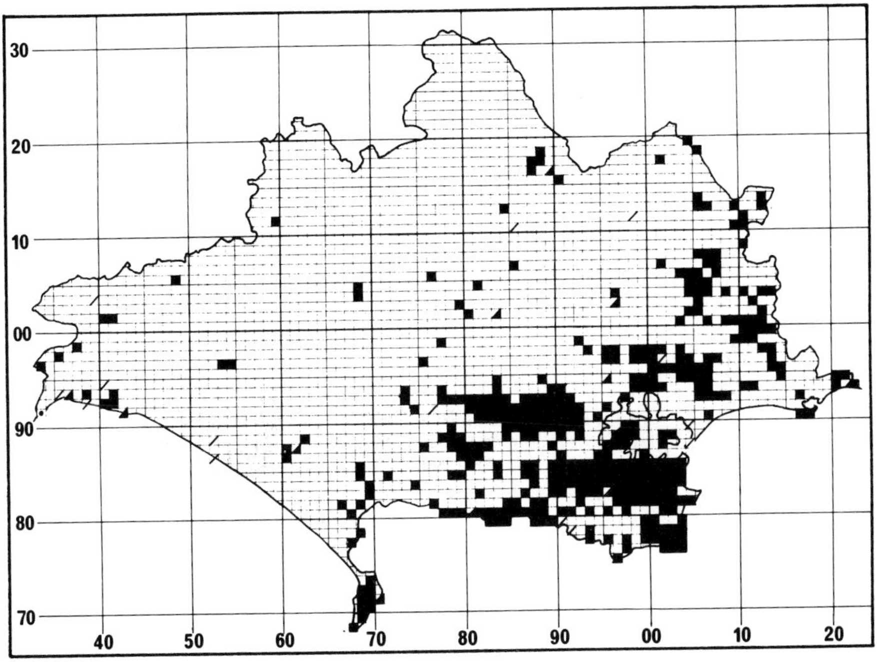

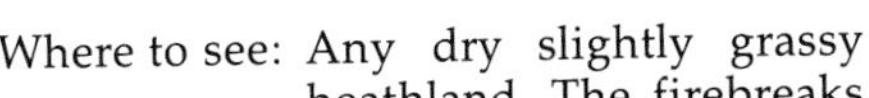

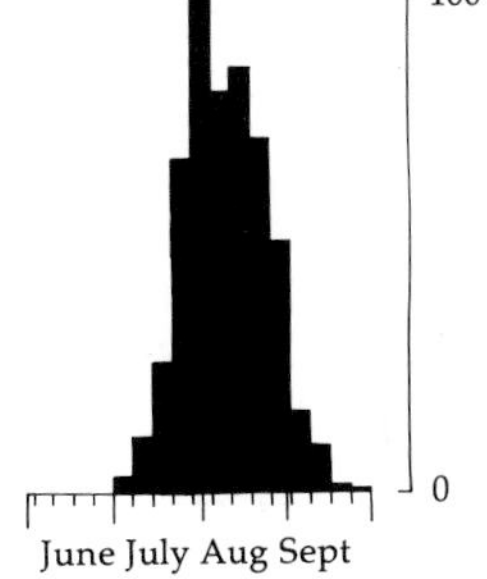

Where to see: Any dry slightly grassy heathland. The firebreaks around Wareham Forest.

When to see: There is one generation of adults a year beginning in early July and reaching a peak about three weeks later.

GATEKEEPER – *Pyronia tithonus* Plate 51

The Gatekeeper or Hedge Brown is one of the commonest and most widely distributed butterflies in Dorset. It flies for the about two months in midsummer and may be seen almost anywhere where shrubs exist with wild grasses growing beneath them. Despite its considerable abundance, it is not a mobile butterfly like the Small Tortoiseshell and Large White but remains in its breeding area. It is unlikely therefore to be seen in town gardens and is largely absent from the urban areas of Poole and Bournemouth.

Many naturalists confuse this species with the Meadow Brown but with practice they are easy to distinguish. The Gatekeeper is somewhat smaller, and is more golden in appearance, especially on the upperwings of the male which also have a large band of dark scent cells on each forewing. The female Gatekeepers are paler and slightly duller. Both sexes have a jerky flight and seem to hop between bramble blossoms, ragwort and other favourite flowers. The eggs are laid in semi-shaded places beneath shrubs. The larva feeds on wild grasses, although it is not known exactly which species. Fine grasses such as the bents (*Agrostis* spp.) are believed to be preferred. As with most browns, the blades of the grass must grow quite tall before they are acceptable to this butterfly. This is usually the case beneath shrubs, where the ground flora is protected from mowing or grazing.

Distribution and Status

Colonies occur on all soils throughout Dorset wherever there are shrubs and rough grass. It is often the most abundant butterfly along the shrubby edges of woods (including conifer plantations) and in open rides and glades. Equally large numbers breed on scrubby cliffs and undercliffs. It is also a familiar sight, although at lower densities, along hedgerows and lanes throughout the County. Unlike the Meadow Brown, it is abundant on many heaths, especially where there is some grass and gorse scrub. It is less common, but often present, on pure heather areas. It is generally absent from open unhedged downland, although isolated shrubs may harbour a few individuals.

The map of this species is clearly incomplete, especially in the west and north of Dorset. The Gatekeeper is genuinely scarce on the intensively cultivated chalklands of central Dorset and must have been much commoner before hedgerows were removed. It is largely absent from the urban areas. Elsewhere there is little reason to believe that it has changed in status; both Dale and Parkinson Curtis considered that it was too common to warrant comment.

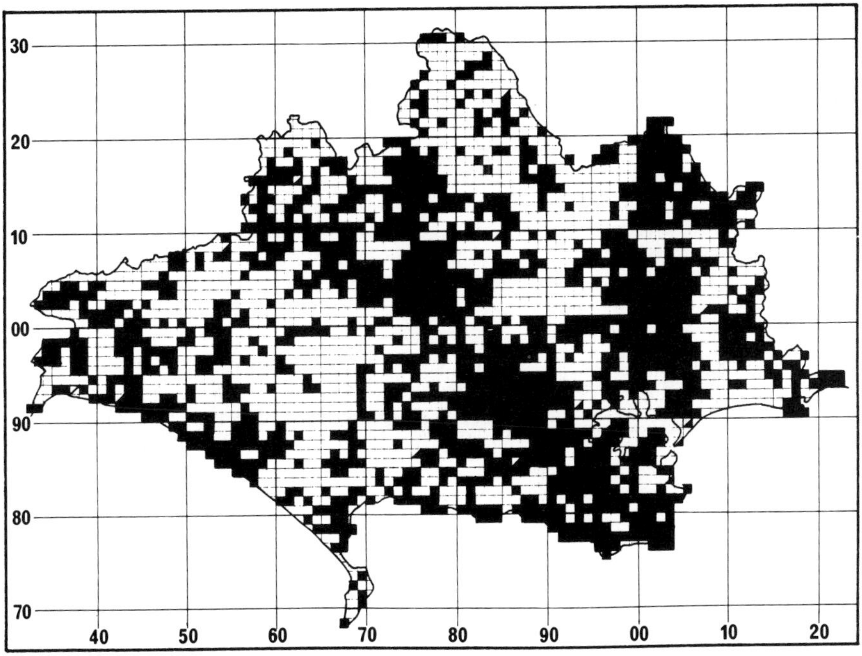

Where to see: Woodedges, rides, hedgerows and scrubby areas anywhere in Dorset.

When to see: The flight period is shorter than the Meadow Brown, beginning later and ending earlier. Peak numbers occur in late July and early August. The histogram shows the flight period from a chalk locality where, like the Meadow Brown, it lasts two to three weeks longer than on other soils.

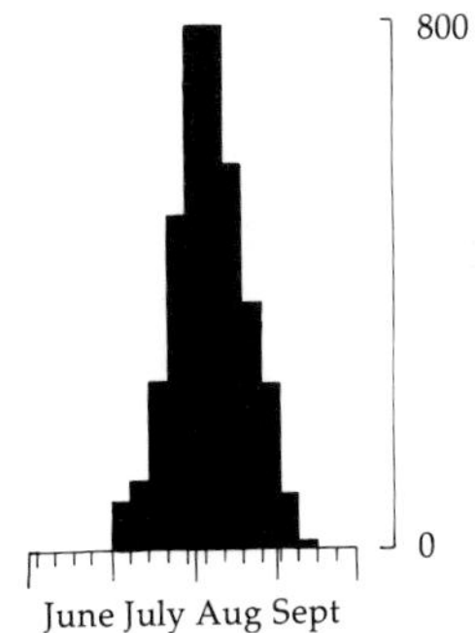

MEADOW BROWN – *Maniola jurtina* Plate 49

The Meadow Brown is another one of the commonest and most widely distributed butterflies in Dorset. The relatively large adult, with its floppy drunken flight is a familiar sight throughout the summer in almost all places where wild grasses grow. The male is the more uniformly marked of the sexes; it is dark, grey-brown with little eyespots on the forewings. The female is larger, with more orange markings and bigger 'eyes'. There is one, very long, adult emergence each year, which lasts from June to October on chalk downland, but for some unexplained reason, the butterfly is over much earlier in other habitats and is rarely seen after mid August. The eggs are laid singly, sometimes on grassleaves or dead vegetation, sometimes just dropped on the ground. The larva eats grass and overwinters when quite small. It resumes feeding in the spring, hiding at the base of a grass clump by day, and ascending to feed at night. As with other Browns, it is easy to find the long green larvae by searching tall grass by torchlight in April.

The range of grasses eaten by the caterpillar is still unknown, but Smooth Meadow Grass (*Poa pratensis*) is a favourite, whereas coarse grasses are less acceptable. The best breeding sites generally have swards of the finer grasses, where the turf grows quite tall and yet is open. Enormous populations of tens and possibly hundreds of thousands of adults may develop where such grassland occurs, for example on many lightly grazed or recently abandoned downs and on the cliffs and undercliffs that are not dominated by Tor Grass. In contrast, neither tall dense swards nor very short ones support many, if any, Meadow Browns. Quite compact colonies may be formed and the butterflies rarely fly far from their breeding sites. A colony can be supported by a very small or even thin area of suitable grassland. Thus adults may be seen feeding on bramble and other hedgerow flowers, since hedge bases provide adequate habitats, as do small corners of tallish grass. However, except in the countryside, this butterfly is unlikely to be seen on garden flowers. Modern housing estates, well kept lawns and urban areas are all unsuitable, as the lack of records from the well recorded Poole and Bournemouth areas shows. The Meadow Brown is one of the most abundant butterflies in woods on all soils, breeding in rides, glades and grassy areas. Today this species is more numerous in woods than intensively cultivated farmland, since it has been eliminated from most improved arable areas and leys, except for small numbers along hedge banks.

Distribution and Status

The map is far from complete, especially in the west and north of the County. The Meadow Brown is scarce or even absent from intensively cultivated farmland on the chalk around Dorchester, Blandford and Wimborne. It is also scarce on heathland, being confined to tracks and edges and virtually absent from large urban areas. Small colonies exist along hedges and verges almost everywhere else and at the edges of and within most woods in the County. The largest populations exist on lightly grazed, unimproved dowland and along the coast.

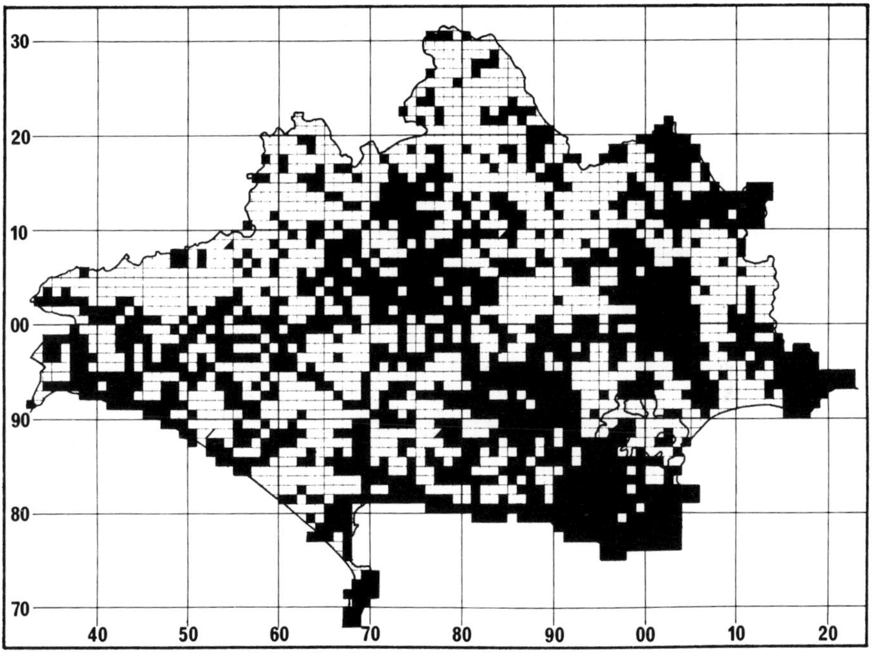

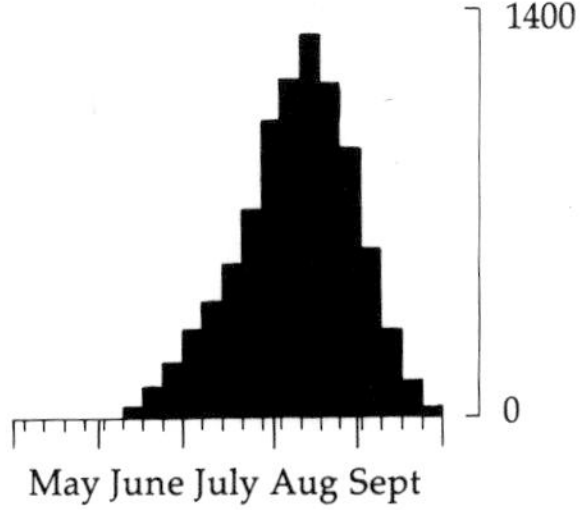

Where to see: Feeding on flowers in any tallish, uncultivated grassland.

When to see: Mid June to mid August, extending to late September on the chalk.

SMALL HEATH – *Coenonympha pamphilus* Plate 50

The Small Heath is one of the most widely distributed butterflies in the County but, unlike other Browns, it is rarely seen in large numbers and is therefore overlooked. It is the smallest Brown; the undersides of the hindwings are a somewhat drab grey-brown while those of the forewings are orange. The uppersides are tawny-orange but are only exposed in flight. It is an active little butterfly and is on the wing from late spring until autumn. There is a complicated sequence of broods which has not been definitively described, but it is sufficient to know that, in Dorset, the Small Heath may be seen anytime from May to October with two peaks of abundance; one in early summer, the other smaller one in September (see opposite).

Although seemingly ubiquitous in most natural habitats, the Small Heath breeds in discrete colonies and the adults are mainly sedentary. Colonies are small and contain a few tens of adults. The eggs are laid on the grasses which form the larval foodplants although, like most Browns, the full range of species eaten is not known. The fine leaved grasses, such as the bents and fescues are considered to be the favourites. The Small Heath is commonest in Dorset on well drained soils, where these grasses abound, such as chalk and limestone downs, on eroding cliffs and undercliffs, and on dunes and heaths. In the latter habitats, grassy places, such as on recently burnt areas, where Bristle Bent (*Agrostis curtisii*) is abundant are chosen. Parkinson Curtis studied the variation in the Small Heath from many habitats and agreed with Bankes that heathland specimens, especially those from the damper areas, were unusually large and brightly coloured in Dorset. The butterfly is less numerous in taller, denser grasslands, but is usually present in small numbers. Thus, colonies breed along many road verges and hedge banks and in rough grass along the edges and within woods.

Distribution and Status

All previous recorders considered the Small Heath to be one of the commonest butterflies in Dorset: common (Dale); common everywhere (Haines); generally common in Purbeck (Bankes); 'I hardly have failed to see this insect at a suitable time except where the land is definitely under bricks and mortar, the plough or the nursery garden. A list of localities would be a superfluity' (Parkinson Curtis). We shall add, to Parkinson Curtis' list of destructive agents, land that has been agriculturally improved, which today covers most farmland in Dorset and virtually all of the flatter areas. Nevertheless, the Small Heath is extremely well distributed, and the map greatly under-represents its occurrence, although it reflects the relative abundances in the different regions. It is commonest along the coast and in Portland, on the steep chalk downs from Swanage to Dorchester and north-eastwards to Shaftesbury and Martin, and on all the surviving heathland, including grassy areas around conifer plantations. It is less common, but survives, along hedgerows and in woods on the flatter areas of chalk and on the heavy clays of north Dorset.

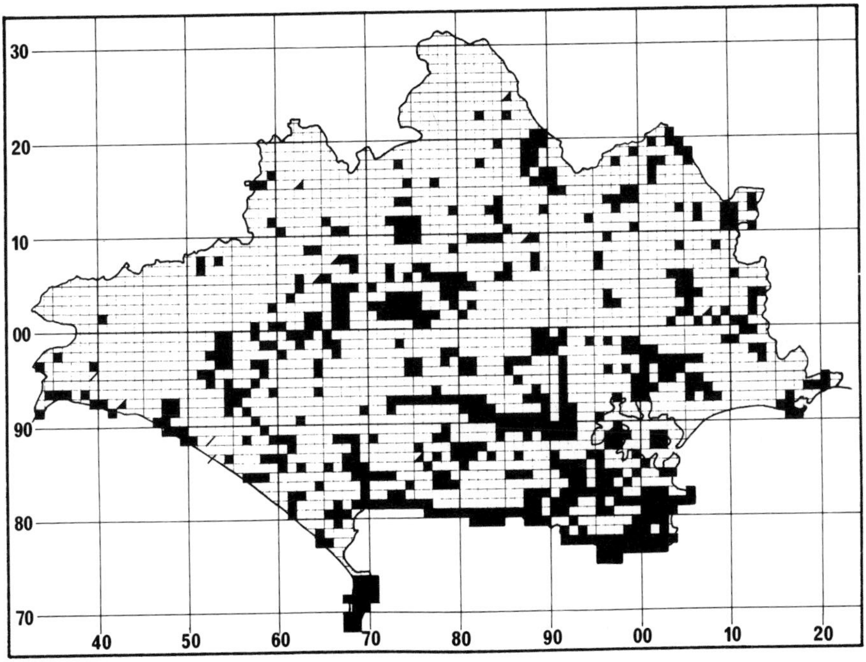

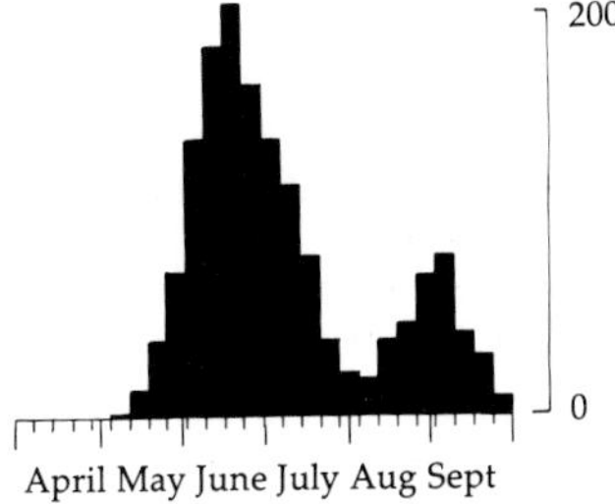

Where to see: Any grassland where fine leaved native species predominate.

When to see: May to October, with peaks of abundance in late June and early September.

RINGLET – *Aphantopus hyperantus* Plate 55

The Ringlet is fairly common in Dorset but is more locally distributed than the other Browns, except the Grayling. It may be seen flying in summer in all districts of the County, mainly in woods or along hedgerows. It is frequently overlooked; faded specimens can be mistaken for the Meadow Brown, with which it usually flies. On close examination, the Ringlet is easy to identify. It has very dark wings; those of fresh males appear almost black when they are open. However, except in dull weather, it sits with its wings closed. This reveals its most distinctive feature, a series of small, white-centred eyespots that are conspicuous against the dark, burnished undersides of the hind and forewings.

Ringlets breed in self-contained colonies that can be supported by small areas of rough grassland. The eggs are dropped onto the ground and the caterpillars feed on native grasses. The range of species is small but unknown. After hibernating, the caterpillar grows slowly, feeding on grass blades by night. It can be found easily by torchlight. It is fully fed by June. Most colonies occur on dampish lush ground, where the grass is tall. They are especially common in woodland edges, glades and rides, where they are often seen visiting bramble flowers. Other colonies occur in bushy places and hedgerows where tall lush grass is half sheltered by shrubs.

Distribution and Status

Dale described the Ringlet as being 'common in woods' in 19th century Dorset; Haines as 'common in all woods' at the turn of the century; while Parkinson Curtis added that it was 'by no means confined to woods and distinctly local'. The map suggests that colonies now occur throughout Dorset but are very local in many areas. However, we believe that this butterfly has not been recorded fully, especially in the north-west. Colonies occur in local damp spots where there are shrubs on all geological formations but are absent from open dry heathland, open chalk downs and intensively cultivated farmland. There is probably a colony in every wood in the County, apart from middle-aged and mature conifer plantations. The best colonies breed in open broad-leaved woodlands and lush scrubby places on the northern clays and may contain hundreds and probably thousands of individuals. Much smaller colonies breed along many hedgerows and verges in this region and in the damper areas of the west. Although still a fairly common and widespread butterfly, there is little doubt that there are fewer colonies than in former times because of changes in land use and agriculture.

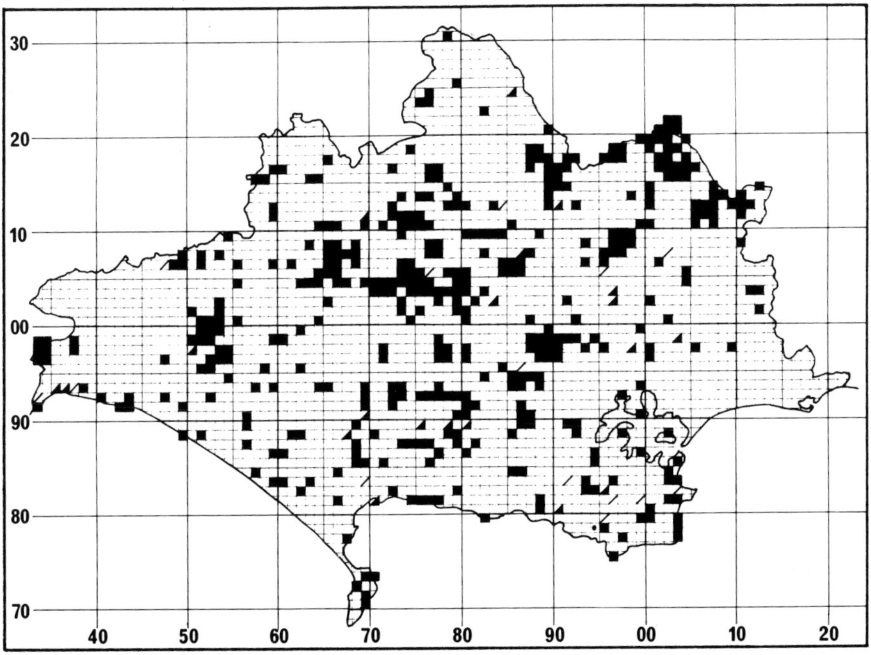

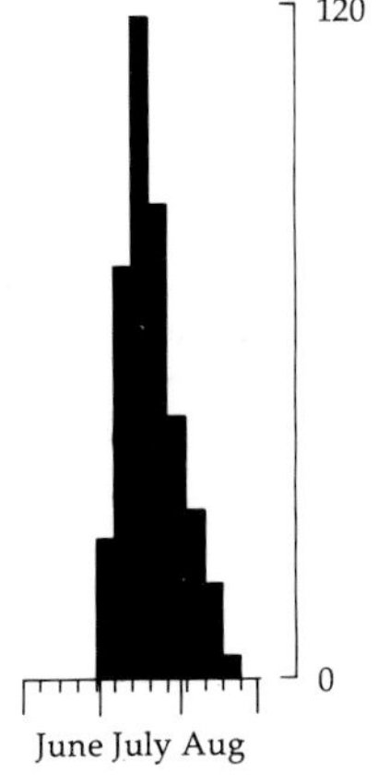

Where to see: Patches of tall damp grassland; in all open woodlands in the Blackmoor Vale.

When to see: Adults emerge at the beginning of July and there is a peak in numbers in the middle of that month. A small number of faded individuals linger into August.

EXTINCT BUTTERFLIES

About six species of butterfly have become extinct in Dorset since records were first collected. We cannot be sure of the exact number because the original status of several of these species is uncertain; some may have entered the lists because of recording errors and others were, perhaps, migrants that became established only temporarily. The fact that only one extinction, that of the Large Tortoiseshell, has occurred this century should not lead to complacency. Many species are declining in abundance and several are under threat.

Swallowtail – *Papilio machaon*

The British subspecies (*britannicus*) of the Swallowtail is a wetland butterfly and is now confined to the Norfolk Broads, where its caterpillar feeds on Milk-parsley (*Peucedanum palustre*). This species is often bred in captivity and accidentally released, leading to many dubious records. In addition, the European subspecies (*gorganus*), which is more mobile, periodically reaches Britain, mainly Kent. Occasionally it establishes itself for a year or two on downland where the larvae feed on Wild Carrot (*Daucus carota*) and on cultivated carrots.

J. C. Dale took 'several' Swallowtails in Dorset from 1805 and 1815, mostly at Glanvilles Wootton, where 12 were taken on three consecutive days in 1815. His son, C. W. Dale, described it as having been 'in plenty' there up to 1816. There no is reason to believe it was not present before 1805, when Dale was only 14 years old. This wet end of the Blackmoor Vale is an unlikely habitat for the continental subspecies and until recently contained extensive marshes, relicts of which are indicated by the reeds (*Phragmnites australis*) growing in the hedgerows. However, Milk-parsley has never been recorded in Dorset, but nevertheless, these records seem more likely to have been from a resident English colony.

Since then, we know of nineteen records, mainly of the continental subspecies, except for some recent escapes in the 1970s and 1980s. There are records from Poole 1840; Studland 1886 and 1900; ten records throughout the County in 1945; two records in 1946 and three records for 1947. Most of the sightings in 1945 were on the chalk downs and wild larvae were found in at least four localities; Blandford, Bryanston, Harmans Cross (two on carrots) and Dorchester. All of the specimens examined by Parkinson Curtis were of the continental subspecies and it is clear that the Swallowtail established itself in the County for at least three years. Interestingly, all records were of summer, second brood individuals. Since then, there have been the occasional records, one in the 1950s and 1973. The most recent are of a continental form found dead in a greenhouse at Stoborough and one at Radipole in 1984.

Black-veined White – *Aporia crataegi*

This mobile butterfly was once widespread but very local in Britain and last bred in Kent in the 1920s. It was barely established in Dorset when records began and the last known capture in the County is generally accepted as that by Dale at Glanvilles Wootton on the 10th June 1815. There is a strange reference to its being taken and seen quite commonly by W. F. Johnson in 1890 at Weymouth. Doubt must be attached to this record since the species had become extinct at its nearest stronghold in the New Forest some 15 years earlier. If genuine, these may have been released individuals, a common practice, then as now.

Large Blue – *Maculinea arion*

Records of the Large Blue are extremely difficult to decipher, since no butterfly has been more subjected to hopeful misidentification and fraud. Parkinson Curtis rigorously examined records from Dorset over five pages of manuscript and we refer the interested reader to these. We have also had the great benefit of G. M. Spooner's unpublished and sound interpretation of old Large Blue records; J. A. Thomas has also had considerable experience of this minefield.

Discounting several very recent nonsenses, prompted by press articles, there are three 19th century records: Charmouth, possibly up to 1848; Chickerell, 1874; Parley Heath in plenty on the 5th August 1834. We agree with Parkinson Curtis who says of the Parley Heath record, 'I frankly disbelieve.' The date and the habitat are wrong and Parkinson Curtis speculates at length that these might possibly have been the closely related Alcon Blue (*Maculinea alcon*), which has never been reliably recorded in Britain, but which uses the Marsh Gentian (*Gentiana pneumonanthe*), which grows on Parley Heath, as a food plant. This is possible but we doubt it. The record from Chickerell is possible, but unlikely, and it is generally rejected. If the species had been there it had disappeared by 1877. The record from Charmouth is accepted. A specimen was taken there by B. A. Morris in 1830 and it reputedly flew 'in plenty' there before 1829. The locality was Stonebarrow Lane and the habitat, though now unsuitable, seems very likely. Interestingly, both Parkinson Curtis and Spooner found that rumours of a special big blue butterfly persisted among non-entomological locals more than a century after the last definite record from Stonebarrow Hill.

Mazarine Blue – *Cyaniris semiargus*

Dorset was one of the former strongholds of this attractive Blue, which was lost to Britain at the end of the last century. It formed discrete colonies, breeding on clover in flowery meadows on a wide range of soils. Most Dorset records were from the clays but this may be due to the fact that J. C. Dale lived in the Blackmoor Vale.

C. W. Dale considered it to have been 'common in meadows in 1839, when it suddenly disappeared.' Whereas Bankes states 'it was formerly widely distributed and locally common'. It is not a species that is prone to wander and records indicating colonies in the early 19th century exist for Bridport, Powerstock, Glanville's Wootton, Middlemarsh, Hazelbury Bryan, Winfrith, Piddlehinton, Lulworth and West Parley. The only regular records are from the famous colony observed between 1808 and 1841 by J. C. Dale close to his home at Glanville's Wootton, from which it was described as common in at least ten of these years. Bretherton calculated that at least 300 individuals had been noted or caught during this period. Fourteen of them survive, in perfect condition, in the Hope Museum at Oxford in the collections of J. C. and C. W. Dale. There is no satisfactory explanation why the Mazarine Blue became extinct in Dorset, probably in 1841, although Parkinson Curtis discovered a specimen labelled 'Glanville's Wootton, 1859, Dale'. Although now extinct in Britain, the occasional migrant (or released) individual is reported from southern England. There is a record for Lodmoor from 1971.

Large Tortoiseshell – *Nymphalis polychloros*

This butterfly occurred sporadically throughout Dorset in the 19th and early 20th centuries. Dale described it as 'generally distributed but not uncommon'; Bankes as, 'seldom common'. Parkinson Curtis, in our opinion rightly, believed the Large Tortoiseshell to be dependent on immigration from neighbouring counties. Dorset has never been a stronghold, as for example was the New Forest, perhaps due to the paucity of suitable woodland. Nevertheless, Parkinson Curtis lists 23 former localities, mainly in Purbeck. In Dorset, as in the rest of Britain, this species has undergone large fluctuations in abundance; it was comparatively plentiful around 1898-1900 and in 1919-20. The last records known to us are in 1945, when it was abundant elsewhere in Britain and a single individual reported from Winspit in 1969. The Large Tortoiseshell is on the verge of extinction in Britain and may even have disappeared as a resident species. Only immigrants and deliberately released specimens are likely to be seen.

Heath Fritillary – *Mellicta athalia*

In the second edition of *Lepidoptera of Dorsetshire,* C. W. Dale lists the Heath Fritillary as rare, without further qualification. It was omitted from the first edition. There is a single record from Charmouth in 1850 by F. Morris. The woods on the poor stony soils in the west of the County were the only likely places for this very rare Fritillary. However, if a colony existed, it has been extinct for a century or more.

RARE MIGRANTS, VAGRANTS AND ACCIDENTAL SPECIES

Since Dorset is one of the southern seaboard counties of England, immigrant Lepidoptera, mainly from the Continent, are reported in most seasons. Over the years there have been many such records, which we have attempted to summarise. When dealing with these records it should be borne in mind that collectors frequently breed foreign Lepidoptera in captivity and, occasionally, these may escape or be deliberately released, leading to false records. In the last few years Butterfly Farms have been established at a number of places in southern England and escapes from these may also occasionally occur. This makes it difficult to establish the authenticity of many recent records.

Chequered Skipper – *Carterocephalus palaemon*

This is not a migratory species, but the record is so unsatisfactory that we include it in this section, rather than among the extinct species. According to Bankes, the Revd. O. Pickard Cambridge pencilled into 'his interleaved Stainton's Manual . . .' two examples at Bloxworth many years ago (now 1886)'. Although he made no note of the captures at the time, and never labelled his insects, both Bankes and Parkinson Curtis gave Pickard Cambridge the benefit of the doubt. There is another record by J. H. Fowler for Swanage in 1899 (*Entomologist*, **32,** 309) but this later proved to be based on hearsay and was withdrawn.

Pale Clouded Yellow – *Colias hyale*
Berger's Clouded Yellow – *Colias australis*

Berger's Clouded Yellow was recognised as a species separate from the Pale Clouded Yellow in 1947, and it is impossible to distinguish it from most old records of the Pale Clouded Yellow. Moreover, the *helice* form of the Clouded Yellow, which resembles both species, is far commoner than either in Dorset, and is often mistaken for them. Indeed, both Bankes and Parkinson Curtis were inclined to disbelieve any record of a Pale (or Berger's) Clouded Yellow that had not been netted. Bearing this in mind, the records show that both species are exceedingly rare in Dorset, more so than in most other counties. Over 56 individuals of *C. hyale* or *C. australis* have been sighted, with up to 6 during the remarkable Clouded Yellow Year of 1983 at Swanage and Portland. Over half of the sightings throughout the County were made in 1900. The other best years were 1843 ('several'), 1945 (3 records), 1947 (5 records). In addition, they were noted in ones and twos, mainly on the coast, in 1835, 1869, 1877, 1885, 1918, 1924, 1936, 1952, 1964 and 1981. The best years for these species have coincided with an abundance of other rare immigrants.

Bath White – *Pontia daplidice*

To our knowledge, this beautiful migratory White has been recorded in Dorset in 1906, 1945, 1972 and 1981. The sightings in the two latter years were of single individuals, but in 1906 and especially in 1945 immigrants bred in numbers in several localities. Of 1906, W. W. Collins wrote in the *Entomologist*, **71,** 898 : 'I captured the Bath White . . . on the Dorset cliffs, west of Durdle Door . . . I saw what I took to be a great hatch out of *P. daplidice*; it is not possible to say how many – the best of my recollection a couple of hundred or probably more as they were hovering about the upper part of the cliff'. The year 1945 was even more fantastic. Records were made along the coast from Lyme to Poole. Reports for that year include: 'many taken and seen in a clover field, Kinson'; 'many seen and taken' at Lyme Regis; two together at Worth Matravers; 'Many taken in a field on the boundry of Poole and Bournemouth'. In addition there were many single sightings throughout the County in 1945.

Papilio bianor

There is a report from Swanage in 1918 of a single individudal of this Swallowtail, which is a native of eastern Siberia and southern China (see H. J. Gibbens, *Entomologist*, **51,** 45). It is obviously a release or escape.

Long-tailed Blue – *Lampides boeticus*

Meyrick lists five 19th century records from Dorset of this extremely rare immigrant. We know of eight sightings in this century; one in 1926, the remainder in the great migrant year of 1945, when between 19th July and 12th September it was reported from Dorchester, Rempstone, Tyneham, Swanage and Sandbanks.

Bloxworth or Short-tailed Blue – *Everes argiades*

This is one of the rarest immigrant butterflies to Britain. It was first recorded by the Revd. O. Pickard Cambridge from Bloxworth Heath, where his sons took a female on 18th August 1885 and a male two days later. An account of this discovery appears in Volume 7 of the *Proceedings of the Dorset Field Club* and includes a beautiful colour illustration. For many years this species was called the Bloxworth Blue, a name that has, sadly, become unfashionable. Another specimen was taken by a schoolboy, F. Tudor, near Bournemouth on 21st August 1885, but the only records in Dorset since then have been in the great year of 1945 (at Swanage and Branksome) and at Worth Matravers and Winspit in 1952.

Lang's Short-tailed Blue – *Syntarucus pirithous*

One taken by M. C. A. Lyell on 13th June 1938 at Bloxworth; seen and determined by N. D. Riley (W. Parkinson Curtis). This species is a native of north Africa and southern Europe.

Camberwell Beauty – *Nymphalis antiopa*

This beautiful migratory Nymphalid is usually seen in eastern England. In Dorset, we know of about twenty two records since 1877. Almost all were single sightings, but two were recorded in 1885, 1930 (coming in from the sea on 26th August), 1935, 1945 and 1976. Recent records are from Brownsea Island (1971), Ferndown (1976) and Hengistbury Head (1982). The only inland record is from Shaftesbury in 1947. Miss M. Bond has recalled that one was caught in the fruit cage at Tyneham House in 1921. This butterfly passed into the hands of the Draper family of Worbarrow where it became a 'family treasure'. It was included in the design of the memorial east window of Tyneham Church in 1923, where the butterfly can be still seen sitting on the blue robe of the Virgin Mary.

Queen of Spain Fritillary – *Argynnis lathonia*

Most records of this rare migrant are from the south-east of England. There are 18 records for Dorset, of which 6 are from the 1940s with four in 1949. Since then there has been one record of an individual seen on two days in a garden in the Bladen Valley at Briantspuddle.

Cardinal or Mediterreanean Fritillary – *Argynnis pandora*

The range of this species extends from the Canary Islands through North Africa and southern Europe to southern Russia. It has occasionally been recorded as an immigrant in Britain. There is a single record for Dorset from Durdle Door on the 13th July 1969 by C. J. D. Sansom (see *Bulletin of the Amateur Entomologists Society*, **29**, 108).

Glanville Fritillary – *Melitaea cinxia*

This small Fritillary is now resident in Britain only on the south coast of the Isle of Wight, about 15 miles south-east of Dorset. There are records of single individuals from south-west Dorset in 1871, from Hod Hill in 1950 and 1954, and Swanage in the 1970s. The 19th century record is rejected by Bankes and Parkinson Curtis, but the others are genuine. It seems certain that these individuals have escaped, or were deliberately released. This was certainly the opinion of the recorder of the 1954 specimen. These butterflies are often bred from larvae collected in the Isle of Wight and we have encountered several examples of escapes and releases. It is certain that no colony has existed in Dorset during this century.

Monarch or Milkweed – *Danaus plexippus*

This large, conspicuous and somewhat slow-flying butterfly is an active migrant and occasionally reaches Britain from North America or the Canary Islands. Most sightings are of single individuals, but as with all immigrant Lepidoptera, good years occur when fair numbers are reported. There are three records of the Monarch for Dorset from the 19th century and the first 20th century record was 1929. In 1933 there were ten reported. Of these, five were seen two miles off the coast flying towards land on the 14th July, and a sixth was seen at sea on the 19th August. Later records are mostly of single specimens until 1969, when some numbers were reported from Langton Matravers, Studland Heath, Dorchester, Wyke Regis, Portland, Bridport and Sturminster Newton. Up to ten individuals at a time were reported feeding on Michaelmas Daisies, from both Dorchester and Sturminster Newton. The next influx was in 1981 when Monarchs appeared in the Isles of Scilly and most south-western counties. In Dorset, they were sighted at five or six localities from Burton Bradstock to Brownsea Island, and an inland record from the north-west of the County. There are records from Durleston for 1982 and from Portland and Dorchester in 1983.

CONSERVATION

The changes in abundance experienced by most species of butterfly in Dorset have already been described. In many cases, this has been linked to major or minor alterations in the way in which the countryside is being used and managed. Table 2, which excludes the Essex Skipper and the three common migrants, reveals that whilst three species have increased in numbers during the past 30 years, three quarters of the butterflies in the County have declined. These decreases have been well documented only for the local species but even this group accounts for half of Dorset's butterflies. The greatest declines have been for the sedentary species that

Table 2. Extinct species, and changes in status during the past 30 years.

Extinct species	Declines: more than two-thirds colonies lost	Declines: heavy but unquantified
Black-veined White	Silver-spotted Skipper	Grizzled Skipper
Swallowtail	White-letter Hairstreak	Dingy Skipper
Mazarine Blue	Adonis Blue	Wood White
Large Blue	Duke of Burgundy	Purple Hairstreak
Large Tortoiseshell	Marsh Fritillary	Green Hairstreak
Heath Fritillary	High Brown Fritillary	Chalkhill Blue
	Small Pearl-bordered Fritillary	Common Blue
	Pearl-bordered Fritillary	Brown Argus
		Silver-studded Blue
		Small Blue
		Silver-washed Fritillary
		Dark Green Fritillary
		Grayling
6 species	8 species	13 species

breed in either the early successional stages of woodland, or in semi-natural grasslands that are well grazed or sparsely vegetated. Species depending on tall grassland have declined less and the mobile species, with the exception of the Large Tortoiseshell, are holding their own. The two butterflies of shady woods have increased in numbers.

If present trends continue, we predict that the High Brown Fritillary, Pearl-bordered Fritillary, Duke of Burgundy and Small Pearl-bordered Fritillary will be lost in this order from commercial woodland in Dorset. These may be followed by the Silver-washed Fritillary, as has already happened in many of the counties of eastern England. Among the grassland species, the Adonis Blue has recently experienced a respite from its rapid decline in the three decades since 1950. Nevertheless, we believe that its survival in the medium and long term is threatened. We expect the Marsh Fritilliary soon to disappear from its wet farmland sites. These and some other species are likely to survive in Dorset only on nature reserves where their habitats are deliberately maintained. The Wood White and the Silver-spotted Skipper are already restricted to nature reserves. There is also a large number of other species that will continue to decline as fundamental changes destroy their habitats. For most, the decline may be checked since they should be able to survive in such places as the coast, National Trust properties, and the Army ranges. They may also survive on farms that have steep hills, occasional rough corners and cover for game. Roadsides, hedgerows and banks may also provide limited areas of habitat which will also help to check the decline of a few species. However, we expect most common species to be eliminated from most fields.

It is beyond the scope of this book to argue whether the habitats of threatened species should be deliberately maintained in the form of nature reserves, which to

Inferred declines of common species	Little or no change	Increase
Large Skipper	Brimstone	Lulworth Skipper
Small Skipper	Small White	White Admiral
Orange Tip	Large White	Speckled Wood
Green-veined White	Brown Hairstreak	
Small Copper	Holly Blue	
Ringlet	Purple Emperor	
Small Heath	Comma	
Gatekeeper	Peacock	
Meadow Brown	Small Tortoiseshell	
Marbled White		
Wall		
11 species	9 species	3 species

some extent are museum sites. We feel strongly that they should, both for the enormous pleasure that they give to people, and to maintain populations from which colonisation of other areas can take place. For example, the recent spread of the Adonis Blue onto new areas of downland which have recently been grazed, was only possible because of the survival of a few nearby relict populations.

Fortunately in Dorset, we have not yet experienced the massive extinctions of butterflies that have occurred in the eastern counties of England, or as in the case of the Netherlands, over an entire country. Fortunately too, there is a wide range of protected areas, which includes country parks, National Trust properties, Army ranges and over 50 nature reserves. Few, if any, of the nature reserves in Dorset were established to conserve insects. Nevertheless, the reserves at Fontmell Down, Powerstock Common, and Brackett's Coppice are each known to have 35-40 species of butterflies and, together with Durleston Country Park, are outstanding sites for butterflies in national terms. Indeed, butterflies are surprisingly well represented on reserves in the County, although it would be desirable if this could be even higher. Only the High Brown Fritillary, Purple Emperor and Brown Hairstreak have not been recorded on any of the reserves. The number of nature reserves on which locally distributed species are known to breed is listed in Table 3.

	DNT	NNR	RSPB	LNR	Parks	Total
Lulworth Skipper	2	1			1	4
Silver-spotted Skipper	2					2
Wood White	2					2
Green Hairstreak	6	4	1		2	13
Purple Hairstreak	2		1		1	4
White-letter Hairstreak	4				1	5
Small Blue	5	1	1		1	8
Silver-studded Blue	1	3	1			5
Brown Argus	9	2	1		1	13
Common Blue	14	4	2	1	2	23
Chalkhill Blue	9				1	10
Adonis Blue	4	1			1	6
Holly Blue	9	4	2	1	2	18
Duke of Burgundy	3					3
White Admiral	3	3	1			7
Pearl-bordered Fritillary	2	1				3
Small Pearl-bordered Fritillary	4	2	1			7
Dark Green Fritillary	9	2	1		1	13
Silver-washed Fritillary	5	3	1		1	10
Marsh Fritillary	4					4
Marbled White	13	1	2		2	18
Grayling	5	4	1	1	1	12

Table 3. The occurrence of species of butterfly of special conservation interest on different types of nature reserves in Dorset.

Many of the British colonies of Adonis Blue, Silver-studded Blue, Grayling and Small Blue are concentrated in Dorset and therefore from a national point of view, are of the utmost importance. This is even truer of the Lulworth Skipper, although this species is not under threat so long as the undercliffs remain unstable. The few colonies in Dorset of Silver-spotted Skipper, High Brown Fritillary, Duke of Burgundy, Wood White, Purple Emperor and Brown Hairstreak are also of national importance, and so is the Marsh Fritillary, which has already been eliminated over large area of Europe.

To keep viable populations of these butterflies, nature reserves have to be managed to provide optimum habitats. It is apparent from the earlier accounts that many species require particular successional stages of plant communities. These communities are dynamic; they gradually change from pioneer species to herb-dominated swards, to scrub, and ultimately to woodland. In the past, the activities of man and his animals (in a few cases because of the type of soil or the climate) arrested this succession, thereby providing the habitats required by many species of butterfly. Practices such as coppicing and the grazing of unimproved downland are good examples of these arresting factors. Nowadays in their absence, management for nature conservation must attempt to resume them or to find substitutes for them. Even where we can manage a reserve on a general scale by these practices, it may be necessary to undertake small scale management to meet the exact needs of some species.

That is the theory of conservation management: it is much easier said that done. Knowledge of the exact habitat requirements of many species is far from complete and even where these are known, the practical problems may be formidable, despite the fact that colonies of many species can exist on very small areas of suitable land. An insect colony is much more likely to be extinguished by a single act of mismanagement or by delaying management than is the case, for example, with perennial plants. For a sedentary insect, local extinctions may be permanent because surviving colonies are often too far away for recolonisation to happen. However much knowledge and practice improve, occasional extinctions are likely to occur on nature reserves. These could be made good by deliberate introductions, a point which will be discussed later. Despite such difficulties, successes have outnumbered losses on the nature reserves in Dorset and where management has provided suitable conditions, increases have been rapid and spectacular.

Outside of nature reserves, for instance on farmlands and in commercial woodland, there is enormous scope to improve the habitats of butterflies. We hope that the information given in each of the species accounts will be helpful for this purpose. Much could be made of road verges and especially of banks and cuttings on new roads across the chalk. A first attempt has been made by the County Council at Bere Regis, where fine grasses, Trefoil and Vetch seeds have been sown. This cutting already has fine colonies of Marbled White and other Browns, Common Blue and Skippers, despite lying in the an intensively farmed region where butterflies are otherwise scarce.

There is considerable scope, too, for introducing scarce species to temporary or new habitats on commercially managed land; for instance when a pit or quarry is exhausted, a field abandoned, or for the first 10-20 years after a wood is felled. Such places are rarely colonised by local sedentary species. At present there are several places in Dorset that appear to be suitable for the small Fritillaries, the Marsh

Fritillary, Duke of Burgundy, Small Blue, Adonis Blue and Wood White but which do not possess colonies probably because they are too far from existing populations. The successful introduction of the Wood White to Powerstock Common is a good example. This introduction is all the more welcome since the site from which the founding butterflies were taken is now unsuitable and the colony thought to be extinct. However, the subject of introductions is a controversial one and no introduction should be attempted without the advice and approval of the Nature Conservancy Council.

Butterfly collecting is another controversial subject that can be discussed only briefly. For adults we advocate photography, using a single lens reflex camera, as a cheaper, safer and more enjoyable alternative, and one during which one learns much more about the behaviour of the different species. Photography may not be realistic for children: rearing butterflies from eggs is thoroughly recommended.

Collecting is often wrongly discussed in emotional terms. The practice is obnoxious to many – it is to us – yet there is no scientific case for claiming that moderate, responsible collecting has the slightest effect on large colonies of butterflies in good habitats, any more than a vigorous hedge is harmed by cutting. Numbers are made up rapidly in the succeeding generations by the increased survival of the remaining individuals. However, small colonies of sedentary species can undoubtedly be extinguished by persistent, irresponsible collecting. Because of their scarcity, vulnerability, colony structure and behaviour, we consider that the following species should not be collected at all, in Dorset:

Silver-spotted Skipper	Marsh Fritillary
Wood White	High Brown Fritillary
Small Blue	Pearl-bordered Fritillary
Duke of Burgundy	Small Pearl-bordered Fritillary

Collecting is, of course, banned on all nature reserves and National Trust properties and in many other places as well. If you do collect, you should follow *A Code for Insect Collecting* written by the Joint Committee for the Conservation of British Insects.

Many people wish to improve their gardens for butterflies; entire books have been written on this subject. We recommend *The Butterfly Gardener* by Miriam Rothschild and Clive Farrell (Michael Joseph, 1983). Although certain flowers can be grown which attract the most mobile butterflies, such as Vanessids and Whites, it is doubtful whether average-sized gardens will ever make a significant contribution as breeding sites for butterflies, except for the Holly Blue and the Large and Small (Cabbage) Whites. For those who wish to make a greater contribution towards conserving butterflies in Dorset, we suggest membership and active participation in the work of The Dorset Naturalists' Trust, 39 Christchurch Road, Bournemouth BH1 3NS. There is also a national society: The British Butterfly Conservation Society, Tudor House, Quorn, Loughborough, Leicestershire LE12 8AD.

Finally, records of butterflies and other wildlife continue to be sought by the Dorset Environmental Records Centre at the County Museum in Dorchester. This is of inestimable value, since it is only with the background knowledge that the Centre provides that future changes can be monitored. The accounts of the butterflies in the County, which we have written, would have been impossible without the records that have already been contributed by so many naturalists in Dorset.

Acknowledgements

It would not have been possible to write the species accounts in this book had it not been for the earlier work of E. R. Bankes and W. Parkinson Curtis, who prepared the ground so thoroughly. We owe an enormous debt to Parkinson Curtis, who in his unpublished manuscript so meticulously reviewed the status of butterflies in Dorset up to 1966. We should like to thank the Dorset County Museum for allowing us to make use of this important work.

For recent records and advice, we are immensely grateful to the large number of naturalists throughout the county who have sent information to the Dorset Environmental Records Centre or to us, and we should like to thank the Centre for its support during this project. In particular, we should like to thank the previous Keeper of Records, Shelia Gowers, who with Simon Hayter, David Walker and other helpers organised the recording scheme and handled many of the records. We are also indebted to the present Keeper, Myra Scott and her team – Mary Newman, Juliet Streatfield and Adrian Moon – who have dealt with all the recent records and have drawn the maps. Susan Westwood helped with the histograms.

We have been fortunate to draw upon data gathered by butterfly monitoring schemes, and for this we should like to thank, L. Clemence, J. R. Cox, P. Merrett, W. G. Shreeves and C. J. Tubb. M. S. Warren has been an invaluable source of information on the history of woodland in the county, and has generously donated some photographs, as has K. J. Willmott.

We are very grateful for the help and advice of Jo Chaplin, Honorary Editor to the Dorset Natural History and Archaeological Society, who organised the publication of this book so efficiently. S. C. S. Brown and Margaret Brooks have kindly provided historical photographs and information.

We wish to record both our own thanks and that of the Dorset Natural History and Archaeological Society to the World Wildlife Fund, who provided a grant towards the costs of preparing the maps and a loan towards the costs of publication.

Index of Species